The Open University

AB4

Power series

The Open University, Walton Hall, Milton Keynes, MK7 6AA.

First published 2006.

Edited, designed and typeset by The Open University, using the Open University TeX System.

Printed and bound in the United Kingdom by Hobbs the Printers Limited, Brunel Road, Totton, Hampshire SO40 3WX.

ISBN 0 7492 0214 9

1.1

Contents

Introduction

The evaluation of functions is of great importance. If we are dealing with a *polynomial* function, then the calculation of its values is just a matter of arithmetic. For example, if

$$f(x) = 1 + \tfrac{1}{2}x - \tfrac{1}{2}x^2 - \tfrac{1}{6}x^3 + \tfrac{1}{4}x^4,$$

then

$$f(1) = 1 + \tfrac{1}{2} - \tfrac{1}{2} - \tfrac{1}{6} + \tfrac{1}{4} = \tfrac{13}{12}.$$

On the other hand, the sine function is different; there is no way of calculating most of its values exactly just by the use of arithmetic.

This unit is concerned with a procedure for calculating approximate values of functions, like the sine function, which cannot be found exactly. We show that a certain sequence of polynomials can be used to calculate these values to any desired degree of accuracy. Moreover, we can represent many functions as a sum of a convergent series of powers of x. For example, the polynomial $p(x) = x - x^3/6$ approximates $f(x) = \sin x$ to within 5×10^{-6} for all x in the interval $[0, 0.1]$, and

See Example 2.1 and Theorem 2.3.

$$\sin x = x - \frac{x^3}{3!} + \frac{x^5}{5!} - \frac{x^7}{7!} + \cdots, \quad \text{for } x \in \mathbb{R}.$$

In Section 1 we define the *Taylor polynomial* $T_n(x)$ at a point a of a function f, and discuss several particular functions for which Taylor polynomials appear to provide good approximations.

In Section 2 we investigate how closely the Taylor polynomials of a function f approximate f, and we discuss when f has a representation of the form

$$f(x) = \lim_{n \to \infty} T_n(x) = \sum_{n=0}^{\infty} a_n(x - a)^n;$$

that is, when f is the *sum function* of a *power series* $\sum_{n=0}^{\infty} a_n(x - a)^n$.

In Section 3 we look at the behaviour of power series in their own right, and consider functions which are *defined* by power series. In particular, we see that any power series $\sum_{n=0}^{\infty} a_n(x - a)^n$ behaves in one of three ways:

- it converges only for $x = a$;
- it converges for all x;
- it converges for $|x - a| < R$ and diverges for $|x - a| > R$, where $R > 0$.

In the last case, R is called the *radius of convergence* of the series.

In Section 4 we discuss various rules for manipulating power series, including the Sum, Multiple and Product Rules. We also find that it is valid to differentiate or integrate a given power series term by term, and that these operations do not affect the radius of convergence.

In Section 5 we review many of the ideas introduced in the unit, and discuss various methods for estimating π. Finally, we prove that π is irrational.

Study guide

Sections 1–4 should be read in their natural order.

Section 4 includes the audio section, which introduces various ways of manipulating power series.

Section 5 is the video section. You can watch the video programme at any time during your study of the unit.

This unit contains a large number of proofs, some of which are not particularly illuminating. We have, therefore, indicated that certain subsections containing proofs are optional.

1   Taylor polynomials

After working through this section, you should be able to:

(a) calculate the *Taylor polynomial* $T_n(x)$ at a given point a of a given function f;

(b) appreciate that in many cases $T_n(x)$ gives a good approximation to $f(x)$ for x near the point a.

1.1   What are Taylor polynomials?

Let f be a function defined on an open interval I. Throughout this unit, we assume that a is a particular point of I and seek polynomial functions which provide good approximations to f near the point a.

If f is continuous at a, then the value $f(a)$ is an approximation to the value of $f(x)$ when x is near a, by the definition of continuity; that is,

$$f(x) \simeq f(a), \quad \text{for } x \text{ near } a.$$

In geometric terms, this means that we can approximate the graph $y = f(x)$ near a by the horizontal line $y = f(a)$ through the point $(a, f(a))$. Usually this does not give a very good approximation.

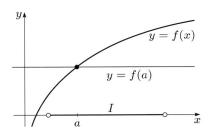

However, if the function f is differentiable on I, then we can obtain what is usually a better approximation by using the tangent at $(a, f(a))$ instead of the horizontal line. The tangent to the graph at $(a, f(a))$ has equation

$$\frac{y - f(a)}{x - a} = f'(a), \quad \text{that is,} \quad y = f(a) + f'(a)(x - a).$$

We can think of the tangent at $(a, f(a))$ as the *line of best approximation* to the graph near a.

So, for x near a, we can write

$$f(x) \simeq f(a) + f'(a)(x - a).$$

This approximation is called the **tangent approximation** at a to f.

Note that the function f and the approximating linear function

$$x \longmapsto f(a) + f'(a)(x - a)$$

have the same value at a and the same first derivative at a, so this is a better approximation to f near a.

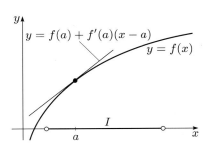

Example 1.1   Determine the tangent approximation at 0 to the function $f(x) = e^x$.

Solution   Here $a = 0$ and

$$f(x) = e^x, \quad f(0) = 1;$$
$$f'(x) = e^x, \quad f'(0) = 1.$$

Hence the tangent approximation at 0 to f is

$$x \longmapsto f(0) + f'(0)(x - 0) = 1 + x. \quad \blacksquare$$

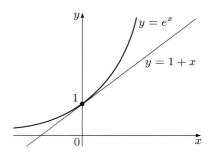

Exercise 1.1   Determine the tangent approximation to each of the following functions f at the given point a.

(a) $f(x) = e^x, \quad a = 2.$ (b) $f(x) = \cos x, \quad a = 0.$

So far we have seen two approximations to $f(x)$ for x near a:

$$f(x) \simeq f(a) \quad \text{(a constant function)};$$
$$f(x) \simeq f(a) + f'(a)(x - a) \quad \text{(a linear function)}.$$

If the function f is twice differentiable on I, then we can consider the quadratic function

$$p(x) = f(a) + f'(a)(x - a) + \tfrac{1}{2}f''(a)(x - a)^2,$$

which is chosen to satisfy $p(a) = f(a)$, $p'(a) = f'(a)$ and $p''(a) = f''(a)$.

It is plausible that, for x near a,

$$f(x) \simeq f(a) + f'(a)(x - a) + \tfrac{1}{2}f''(a)(x - a)^2$$

is a better approximation to f near a. More generally, if the function f is n-times differentiable on I, then we can find a polynomial of degree n whose value at a and first n derivatives at a are equal to those of f, and this polynomial should provide an even better approximation.

On differentiating p, we obtain
$$p'(x) = f'(a) + f''(a)(x - a),$$
$$p''(x) = f''(a).$$

Definition   Let f be n-times differentiable on an open interval containing the point a. Then the **Taylor polynomial of degree n at a for f** is the polynomial

$$T_n(x) = f(a) + f'(a)(x - a) + \frac{f''(a)}{2!}(x - a)^2 + \cdots + \frac{f^{(n)}(a)}{n!}(x - a)^n.$$

The Taylor polynomial also depends on a and f, but our notation $T_n(x)$ does not reflect this.

The coefficients in the definition of T_n have been chosen so that

$$T_n(a) = f(a), \quad T_n'(a) = f'(a), \quad \ldots, \quad T_n^{(n)}(a) = f^{(n)}(a);$$

that is, the functions f and T_n have the same value at a and have equal derivatives at a for all orders up to and including n.

Example 1.2   Determine the Taylor polynomials $T_1(x)$, $T_2(x)$ and $T_3(x)$ at the following points a for the function

$$f(x) = \sin x.$$

(a) $a = 0$ (b) $a = \pi/2$

Brook Taylor (1685–1731) was an English mathematician who published a book in 1715 which included approximation by these polynomials. They were also used by Newton, Leibniz and the Scottish mathematician James Gregory (1638–1675).

Solution   We have

$$f(x) = \sin x, \qquad f(0) = 0, \qquad f(\pi/2) = 1;$$
$$f'(x) = \cos x, \qquad f'(0) = 1, \qquad f'(\pi/2) = 0;$$
$$f''(x) = -\sin x, \qquad f''(0) = 0, \qquad f''(\pi/2) = -1;$$
$$f^{(3)}(x) = -\cos x, \quad f^{(3)}(0) = -1, \quad f^{(3)}(\pi/2) = 0.$$

Hence

(a) $T_1(x) = x$, $T_2(x) = x$, $T_3(x) = x - \frac{1}{6}x^3$;

(b) $T_1(x) = 1$, $T_2(x) = 1 - \frac{1}{2}(x - \pi/2)^2$, $T_3(x) = 1 - \frac{1}{2}(x - \pi/2)^2$.   ∎

We usually do not multiply out brackets in such Taylor polynomials, since that would make the results less clear.

Note that a Taylor polynomial of degree n may sometimes be a polynomial of degree less than n. For instance, in Example 1.2(a) we have $T_2(x) = x$.

Exercise 1.2   Determine the Taylor polynomials $T_1(x)$, $T_2(x)$ and $T_3(x)$ for each of the following functions f at the given point a.

(a) $f(x) = e^x$, $a = 2$.   (b) $f(x) = \cos x$, $a = 0$.

Exercise 1.3   Determine the Taylor polynomial of degree 4 for each of the following functions f at the given point a.

(a) $f(x) = \log_e(1 + x)$, $a = 0$.

(b) $f(x) = \sin x$, $a = \pi/4$.

(c) $f(x) = 1 + \frac{1}{2}x - \frac{1}{2}x^2 - \frac{1}{6}x^3 + \frac{1}{4}x^4$, $a = 0$.

Exercise 1.4   Let T_3 be the Taylor polynomial of degree 3 at 0 for $f(x) = \sin x$. Use your calculator to show that

$$|\sin(0.1) - T_3(0.1)| < 1 \times 10^{-7}.$$

Remember to set your calculator to use angles in radians.

1.2 Approximation by Taylor polynomials

We now look at two specific functions in order to investigate the assertion that Taylor polynomials provide good approximations for a large class of functions.

The function $f(x) = \sin x$

By calculating higher derivatives of the function $f(x) = \sin x$ at 0, we can show that the Taylor polynomials of degrees $1, 2, \ldots, 8$ at 0 for f are:

See Example 1.2(a).

$$T_1(x) = T_2(x) = x, \qquad\qquad T_3(x) = T_4(x) = x - \frac{x^3}{3!},$$

$$T_5(x) = T_6(x) = x - \frac{x^3}{3!} + \frac{x^5}{5!}, \quad T_7(x) = T_8(x) = x - \frac{x^3}{3!} + \frac{x^5}{5!} - \frac{x^7}{7!}.$$

The following graphs illustrate how the approximation to $f(x)$ given by $T_n(x)$ improves as n increases.

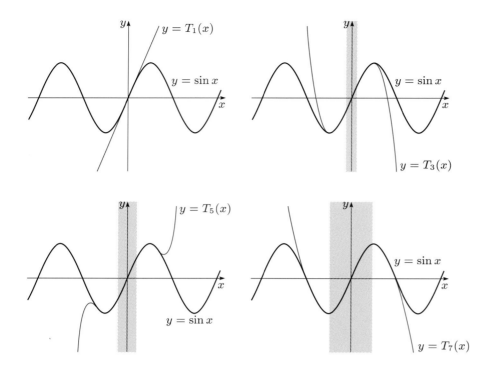

For example, the graph of T_5 appears to be very close to the graph of the sine function over the interval $(-\pi/2, \pi/2)$, so $T_5(x)$ seems to be a good approximation to $\sin x$ in this interval.

It also appears that, as the degree of the Taylor polynomial increases, its graph becomes a good approximation to that of the sine function over a longer interval. For instance, in the above diagrams the shaded area covers the interval of the x-axis on which the Taylor polynomial $T_n(x)$ agrees with $\sin x$ to three decimal places.

The function $f(x) = 1/(1 - x)$

By repeated differentiation of $f(x) = 1/(1 - x)$, we can verify that

$$f^{(k)}(x) = \frac{k!}{(1 - x)^{k+1}}, \quad \text{for } k \in \mathbb{N};$$

thus, in particular, $f^{(k)}(0) = k!$. Hence the Taylor polynomial of degree n at 0 for f is

$$T_n(x) = \sum_{k=0}^{n} \frac{f^{(k)}(0)}{k!} x^k$$

$$= \sum_{k=0}^{n} x^k = 1 + x + x^2 + \cdots + x^n. \tag{1.1}$$

The following diagram shows the graphs of the four Taylor polynomials of degrees 1, 2, 4 and 7 at 0 for f.

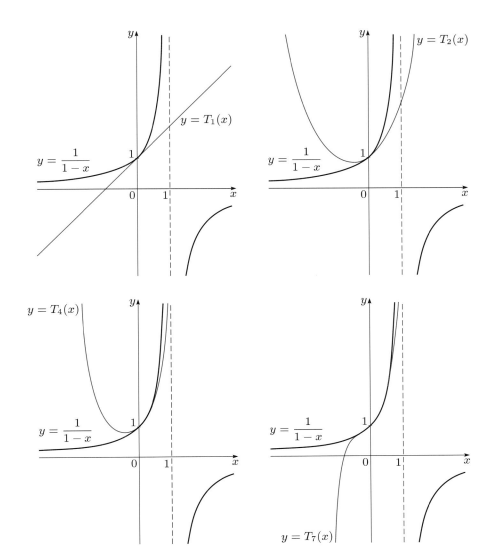

The graphs show that the nature of the approximation is very different from that in the previous example. For the sine function, the interval over which the approximation is good seems to expand indefinitely as the degree of the polynomial increases. For $f(x) = 1/(1-x)$, however, the interval of good approximation always seems to be contained in the interval $(-1, 1)$.

For this function f, the Taylor polynomials $T_n(x)$ at 0 are the nth partial sums of the geometric series $\sum_{n=0}^{\infty} x^n$. This series converges with sum $1/(1-x)$ for $|x| < 1$, and diverges for $|x| \geq 1$. Thus, if $|x| < 1$, then

See Unit AA3, Section 1.

$$T_n(x) \to f(x) \quad \text{as } n \to \infty.$$

So in this example we can prove that the polynomials $T_n(x)$ provide better and better approximations to $f(x)$ as n increases, at least if $|x| < 1$. For $|x| \geq 1$, the sequence $\{T_n(x)\}$ does not converge, so it does not provide an approximation to $f(x)$.

In later sections we often need general formulas for certain key Taylor polynomials, and we ask you to find these in the next exercise.

Exercise 1.5   Determine the Taylor polynomial of degree n at 0 for each of the following functions.

(a) $f(x) = \log_e(1 + x)$ (b) $f(x) = e^x$

(c) $f(x) = \sin x$ (d) $f(x) = \cos x$

Further exercises

Exercise 1.6   Determine the tangent approximation at the following points a to the function

$$f(x) = 2 - 3x + x^2 + e^x.$$

(a) $a = 0$ (b) $a = 1$

Exercise 1.7   For each of the following functions f and points a, find the Taylor polynomial of degree 3 at a for f.

(a) $f(x) = \log_e(1 + x)$, $a = 2$.   (b) $f(x) = \sin x$, $a = \pi/6$.

(c) $f(x) = (1 + x)^{-2}$, $a = \frac{1}{2}$.   (d) $f(x) = \tan x$, $a = \pi/4$.

Exercise 1.8   For each of the following functions f and points a, find the Taylor polynomial of degree 4 at a for f.

(a) $f(x) = \cosh x$, $a = 0$.   (b) $f(x) = x^5$, $a = 1$.

Exercise 1.9   Let T_3 be the Taylor polynomial of degree 3 at 0 for $f(x) = e^x$. Use your calculator to show that

$$|e^{0.1} - T_3(0.1)| < 5 \times 10^{-6}.$$

2   Taylor's Theorem

After working through this section, you should be able to:

(a) state and use Taylor's Theorem;

(b) appreciate that a sequence of Taylor polynomials may or may not converge at a given point to the value of the function at that point;

(c) state and use certain basic Taylor series.

2.1 Taylor's Theorem

In Section 1 we showed how to find the Taylor polynomial $T_n(x)$ of degree n at the point a for a function f. This polynomial and its first n derivatives agree with f and its first n derivatives at a, and for larger values of n the polynomial appears to approximate f at points near a. The following fundamental result gives a formula for the error involved in this approximation.

Theorem 2.1 Taylor's Theorem

Let the function f be $(n + 1)$-times differentiable on an open interval containing the points a and x. Then

$$f(x) = f(a) + f'(a)(x - a) + \cdots + \frac{f^{(n)}(a)}{n!}(x - a)^n + R_n(x),$$

where

$$R_n(x) = \frac{f^{(n+1)}(c)}{(n + 1)!}(x - a)^{n+1},$$

for some c between a and x.

The proof of this theorem is in Subsection 2.3.

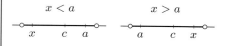

Remarks

1. Taylor's Theorem can be expressed in the form

    $$f(x) = T_n(x) + R_n(x),$$

    where $R_n(x)$ is a *remainder term*, or *error term*, involved in approximating $f(x)$ by $T_n(x)$. The formula for $R_n(x)$ involves an 'unknown number' c, so it does not specify the remainder term $R_n(x)$ exactly. Nevertheless, we can often use it to show that $T_n(x)$ is a good approximation to $f(x)$.

    Strictly speaking, we should use more complicated notation to indicate that the remainder term $R_n(x)$ also depends on a and f.

2. When $n = 0$, Taylor's Theorem reduces to

    $$f(x) = f(a) + f'(c)(x - a),$$

    for some c between a and x; that is,

    $$\frac{f(x) - f(a)}{x - a} = f'(c),$$

    for some c between a and x. But this is just the Mean Value Theorem! Thus Taylor's Theorem can be considered as a generalisation of the Mean Value Theorem.

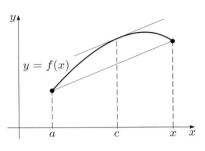

Exercise 2.1   By applying Taylor's Theorem with $n = 3$ to the function $f(x) = \cos x$ at $a = 0$, prove that, for $x \neq 0$,

$$\cos x = 1 - \tfrac{1}{2}x^2 + \frac{\cos c}{4!}\,x^4,$$

where c lies between 0 and x.

The conclusion of Exercise 2.1 can be restated as

$$\cos x - (1 - \tfrac{1}{2}x^2) = \frac{\cos c}{4!}x^4,$$

where c lies between 0 and x. Here we do not know the exact value of c, but we do know that $|\cos c| \leq 1$. Thus we can deduce that

$$\left|\cos x - (1 - \tfrac{1}{2}x^2)\right| = \frac{|\cos c|}{4!}|x|^4 \leq \frac{|x|^4}{4!}.$$

In this way, we obtain an explicit *remainder estimate*, or *error bound*, for the approximation of $\cos x$ by $1 - \tfrac{1}{2}x^2$, which is small when x is near 0.

In general, we can obtain such an estimate for $|f(x) - T_n(x)| = |R_n(x)|$, provided that we have an estimate for $|f^{(n+1)}(c)|$ which is valid for all c between a and x. The following strategy sets out this process.

Strategy 2.1   Applying Taylor's Theorem at a point.

To show that the Taylor polynomial T_n at a for f approximates f to a certain accuracy at a point $x \neq a$, carry out the following.

1. Obtain a formula for $f^{(n+1)}$.

2. Determine a number M such that

    $$|f^{(n+1)}(c)| \leq M, \quad \text{for all } c \text{ between } a \text{ and } x.$$

3. Write down and simplify the remainder estimate

    $$|f(x) - T_n(x)| = |R_n(x)| \leq \frac{M}{(n+1)!}|x - a|^{n+1}.$$

Remark   In step 2, we can use any convenient value for M, preferably not too large. Sometimes, we can determine the maximum value of $|f^{(n+1)}(c)|$ for c in the closed interval with endpoints a and x, but usually any 'good enough' upper bound will do.

Often this maximum value is taken when c is equal to a or x.

Example 2.1

(a) Write down the Taylor polynomial $T_3(x)$ at $a = 0$ for $f(x) = \sin x$.

(b) Use Taylor's Theorem to show that $|\sin(0.1) - T_3(0.1)| < 5 \times 10^{-6}$.

(c) Hence calculate $\sin(0.1)$ to four decimal places.

Solution

(a) For $f(x) = \sin x$ and $a = 0$, we have
$$T_3(x) = x - \tfrac{1}{6}x^3.$$

See the solution to Exercise 1.5(c).

(b) We use Strategy 2.1 with $a = 0$, $x = 0.1$ and $n = 3$.

1. First, $f^{(4)}(x) = \sin x$.

2. Thus
$$|f^{(4)}(c)| = |\sin c| \le 1, \quad \text{for } c \in [0, 0.1],$$
so we can take $M = 1$.

3. Using the remainder estimate $(M/(n+1)!)|x - a|^{n+1}$, we obtain

Here we take $M = 1$, though with care a smaller value for M can be obtained; for example,
$$|\sin c| \le |c| \le 0.1,$$
for $c \in [0, 0.1]$.

$$
\begin{aligned}
|\sin(0.1) - T_3(0.1)| &= |R_3(0.1)| \\
&\le \frac{M}{(3+1)!}|x-a|^{3+1} \\
&= \frac{1}{4!}|0.1 - 0|^4 \\
&= 0.000\,004\,1\overline{6} < 5 \times 10^{-6},
\end{aligned}
$$

as required.

(c) By part (a),
$$
\begin{aligned}
T_3(0.1) &= 0.1 - \tfrac{1}{6} \times 10^{-3} \\
&= 0.1 - 0.000\,166\,66\ldots = 0.099\,833\,33\ldots.
\end{aligned}
$$

By part (b),
$$|\sin(0.1) - T_3(0.1)| = |R_3(0.1)| < 5 \times 10^{-6}.$$

Hence
$$0.099\,828\,33\ldots < \sin(0.1) < 0.099\,838\,33\ldots,$$

so
$$\sin(0.1) = 0.0998 \quad \text{(to 4 d.p.)}. \quad \blacksquare$$

Exercise 2.2

(a) Write down the Taylor polynomial $T_2(x)$ at $a = 0$ for $f(x) = \log_e(1 + x)$.

(b) Use Taylor's Theorem to show that $|\log_e(1.02) - T_2(0.02)| < 3 \times 10^{-6}$.

(c) Hence calculate $\log_e(1.02)$ to four decimal places.

Our next strategy shows how to use Taylor's Theorem to obtain an approximation to f which holds at all points of an interval.

Strategy 2.2   Applying Taylor's Theorem on an interval.

To show that the Taylor polynomial T_n at a for f approximates f to a certain accuracy on an interval I of the form $[a, a+r]$, $[a-r, a]$ or $[a-r, a+r]$, where $r > 0$, carry out the following.

1.   Obtain a formula for $f^{(n+1)}$.

2.   Determine a number M such that
$$|f^{(n+1)}(c)| \le M, \quad \text{for all } c \in I.$$

3.   Write down and simplify the remainder estimate
$$|f(x) - T_n(x)| = |R_n(x)| \le \frac{M}{(n+1)!}\, r^{n+1}, \quad \text{for all } x \in I.$$

We can apply Strategy 2.2 to the situation in Example 2.1 to show that
$$|\sin x - T_3(x)| < 5 \times 10^{-6}, \quad \text{for } x \in [0, 0.1].$$

Here is another example.

Example 2.2

(a)   Calculate the Taylor polynomial $T_3(x)$ at 1 for $f(x) = 1/(x+2)$.

(b)   Show that $T_3(x)$ approximates $f(x)$ with an error less than 5×10^{-3} on the interval $[1, 2]$.

Solution

(a)   For this function,
$$\begin{aligned}
f(x) &= 1/(x+2), & f(1) &= 1/3; \\
f'(x) &= -1/(x+2)^2, & f'(1) &= -1/9; \\
f''(x) &= 2/(x+2)^3, & f''(1) &= 2/27; \\
f^{(3)}(x) &= -6/(x+2)^4, & f^{(3)}(1) &= -2/27.
\end{aligned}$$

Hence the Taylor polynomial of degree 3 at 1 for f is
$$T_3(x) = \tfrac{1}{3} - \tfrac{1}{9}(x-1) + \tfrac{1}{27}(x-1)^2 - \tfrac{1}{81}(x-1)^3.$$

(b)   We use Strategy 2.2 with $I = [1, 2]$, $a = 1$, $r = 1$ and $n = 3$.

1.   First, $f^{(4)}(x) = \dfrac{24}{(x+2)^5}$.

2.   Thus
$$|f^{(4)}(c)| = \frac{24}{(c+2)^5} \le \frac{24}{3^5}, \quad \text{for } c \in [1, 2],$$

Since $c \ge 1$, we have
$c + 2 \ge 1 + 2 = 3$.

so we can take $M = 24/3^5$.

3.   Using the remainder estimate $(M/(n+1)!)r^{n+1}$, we obtain
$$\begin{aligned}
|f(x) - T_3(x)| &= |R_3(x)| \\
&\le \frac{M}{(3+1)!}\, r^{3+1} \\
&= \frac{1}{4!} \times \frac{24}{3^5} \times 1^4 \\
&= \frac{1}{3^5} = 0.0041\ldots, \quad \text{for } x \in [1, 2].
\end{aligned}$$

Thus $T_3(x)$ approximates $f(x)$ with an error less than 5×10^{-3} on $[1, 2]$.   ∎

Exercise 2.3

(a) Calculate the Taylor polynomial $T_4(x)$ at π for the function $f(x) = \cos x$.

(b) Show that $T_4(x)$ approximates $f(x)$ with an error less than 3×10^{-3} on the interval $\left[\frac{3}{4}\pi, \frac{5}{4}\pi\right]$.

2.2 Taylor series

From Taylor's Theorem we know that if a function f can be differentiated as often as we want on an open interval containing the points a and x, then

$$f(x) = T_n(x) + R_n(x) = \sum_{k=0}^{n} \frac{f^{(k)}(a)}{k!}(x-a)^k + R_n(x),$$

for $n = 0, 1, 2, \ldots$, where

$$R_n(x) = \frac{f^{(n+1)}(c)}{(n+1)!}(x-a)^{n+1},$$

for some c between a and x. Thus we have the following result.

Theorem 2.2   Let f have derivatives of all orders on an open interval containing the points a and x. If

$$R_n(x) \to 0 \ \text{ as } n \to \infty,$$

then

$$f(x) = \sum_{n=0}^{\infty} \frac{f^{(n)}(a)}{n!}(x-a)^n. \tag{2.1}$$

For $x = a$ and $n = 0$, this series involves the expression 0^0. By convention, we take $0^0 = 1$ in such series.

Hence, if $R_n(x) \to 0$ as $n \to \infty$, then we can express $f(x)$ as a series whose terms involve powers of $(x-a)$.

Definition   Let f have derivatives of all orders at the point a. The **Taylor series at a for f** is

$$\sum_{n=0}^{\infty} \frac{f^{(n)}(a)}{n!}(x-a)^n = f(a) + f'(a)(x-a) + \frac{f''(a)}{2!}(x-a)^2 + \cdots.$$

If x is a point for which the Taylor series for f has sum $f(x)$, as in equation (2.1), then we say that the Taylor series is **valid** at the point x. Any set of values of x for which a Taylor series is valid is called a **range of validity** for the Taylor series. On any such range of validity, the function f is the **sum function** of the Taylor series.

We can use Theorem 2.2 to obtain the following basic Taylor series. In each case we have indicated a range of validity.

Theorem 2.3 Basic Taylor series

(a) $\dfrac{1}{1-x} = 1 + x + x^2 + \cdots = \displaystyle\sum_{n=0}^{\infty} x^n, \quad \text{for } |x| < 1.$

(b) $\sin x = x - \dfrac{x^3}{3!} + \dfrac{x^5}{5!} - \cdots = \displaystyle\sum_{n=0}^{\infty} \dfrac{(-1)^n x^{2n+1}}{(2n+1)!}, \quad \text{for } x \in \mathbb{R}.$

(c) $\cos x = 1 - \dfrac{x^2}{2!} + \dfrac{x^4}{4!} - \cdots = \displaystyle\sum_{n=0}^{\infty} \dfrac{(-1)^n x^{2n}}{(2n)!}, \quad \text{for } x \in \mathbb{R}.$

(d) $e^x = 1 + x + \dfrac{x^2}{2!} + \cdots = \displaystyle\sum_{n=0}^{\infty} \dfrac{x^n}{n!}, \quad \text{for } x \in \mathbb{R}.$

(e) $\log_e(1+x) = x - \dfrac{x^2}{2} + \dfrac{x^3}{3} - \cdots = \displaystyle\sum_{n=1}^{\infty} \dfrac{(-1)^{n+1} x^n}{n},$

   for $-1 < x \leq 1.$

Proof

(a) Let $f(x) = 1/(1-x)$. The Taylor polynomial of degree n at 0 for f is   *See equation (1.1).*

$$T_n(x) = 1 + x + \cdots + x^n = \sum_{k=0}^{n} x^k.$$

Now $1 + x + x^2 + \cdots$ is a geometric series with initial term 1 and common ratio x, which has sum $1/(1-x)$, for $|x| < 1$, so the result follows.

(b) Let $f(x) = \sin x$. The Taylor polynomial of degree n at 0 for f is   *See the solution to Exercise 1.5(c).*

$$T_n(x) = x - \frac{x^3}{3!} + \cdots + \frac{(-1)^m x^{2m+1}}{(2m+1)!} = \sum_{k=0}^{m} \frac{(-1)^k x^{2k+1}}{(2k+1)!},$$

where $n = 2m + 1$ or $n = 2m + 2$.

By Taylor's Theorem, we have

$$\sin x = T_n(x) + R_n(x), \quad \text{where } R_n(x) = \frac{f^{(n+1)}(c)}{(n+1)!} x^{n+1},$$

for some c between 0 and x. Since

$$f^{(n+1)}(x) = \pm \sin x \text{ or } \pm \cos x,$$ *See the solution to Exercise 1.5(c).*

we have $|f^{(n+1)}(c)| \leq 1$, so

$$|R_n(x)| \leq \frac{|x|^{n+1}}{(n+1)!} \to 0 \text{ as } n \to \infty,$$ *Here we use the Squeeze Rule and the fact that $\{x^n/n!\}$ is a basic null sequence; see Unit AA2, Section 2.*

Hence the result follows.

(c) The proof of part (c) is similar to that of part (b).

(d) Let $f(x) = e^x$. The Taylor polynomial of degree n at 0 for f is   *See the solution to Exercise 1.5(b).*

$$T_n(x) = 1 + x + \frac{x^2}{2!} + \cdots + \frac{x^n}{n!} = \sum_{k=0}^{n} \frac{x^k}{k!}.$$

15

By Taylor's Theorem, we have

$$e^x = T_n(x) + R_n(x),$$

where

$$R_n(x) = \frac{f^{(n+1)}(c)}{(n+1)!} x^{n+1} = e^c \frac{x^{n+1}}{(n+1)!},$$

for some c between 0 and x. Now $e^c \leq e^{|x|}$ and $\{x^{n+1}/(n+1)!\}$ is a null sequence. Hence $R_n(x) \to 0$ as $n \to \infty$, by the Squeeze Rule, so the result follows.

The value of c depends on n, but it always lies between 0 and x.

(e) Let $f(x) = \log_e(1+x)$. The Taylor polynomial of degree n at 0 for f is

$$T_n(x) = x - \frac{x^2}{2} + \frac{x^3}{3} - \cdots + \frac{(-1)^{n+1}x^n}{n} = \sum_{k=0}^{n} \frac{(-1)^{k+1}x^k}{k}.$$

See the solution to Exercise 1.5(a).

By Taylor's Theorem, we have

$$\log_e(1+x) = T_n(x) + R_n(x), \quad \text{where } R_n(x) = \frac{f^{(n+1)}(c)}{(n+1)!} x^{n+1},$$

for some c between 0 and x.

Now suppose that $0 < x \leq 1$. Since

$$f^{(n+1)}(x) = \frac{(-1)^{n+2}n!}{(1+x)^n},$$

See the solution to Exercise 1.5(a).

we have

$$|R_n(x)| = \frac{1}{(n+1)!} \times \frac{n!}{(1+c)^n} |x|^{n+1}$$

$$= \frac{|x|^{n+1}}{(n+1)(1+c)^n} \leq \frac{1}{n} \to 0 \quad \text{as } n \to 0.$$

Since $0 < c < x \leq 1$, we have $|x|^{n+1} \leq 1$ and $1 + c > 1$.

Hence

$$\log_e(1+x) = \sum_{n=1}^{\infty} \frac{(-1)^{n+1}x^n}{n}, \quad \text{for } 0 \leq x \leq 1.$$

The proof that this Taylor series is valid for $-1 < x < 0$ does not follow from the above form of $R_n(x)$; we prove it later in the unit. ∎

See Exercise 4.7(b).

Remarks

1. Taking $x = 1$ in Theorem 2.3(e), we obtain the unexpected sum

$$\sum_{n=1}^{\infty} \frac{(-1)^{n+1}}{n} = 1 - \tfrac{1}{2} + \tfrac{1}{3} - \tfrac{1}{4} + \cdots = \log_e 2.$$

2. Earlier, we defined the exponential function as

See Unit AA3, Subsection 4.1.

$$e^x = \begin{cases} \displaystyle\sum_{n=0}^{\infty} \frac{x^n}{n!}, & x \geq 0, \\ (e^{-x})^{-1}, & x < 0. \end{cases}$$

Theorem 2.3(d) shows that e^x is the sum function of the series $\sum_{n=0}^{\infty} x^n/n!$ for *all* x, not just for $x \geq 0$.

Some texts define $e^x = \exp(x)$ using this power series.

3. In this course, $\sin x$ and $\cos x$ are defined in terms of a right-angled triangle. Theorem 2.3 shows that $\sin x$ and $\cos x$ can be represented by power series; some texts use these series to define $\sin x$ and $\cos x$ in a way that does not depend on geometric ideas.

2.3 Proof of Taylor's Theorem

Earlier we proved the Mean Value Theorem using Rolle's Theorem; we now use a similar approach to prove Taylor's Theorem.

Rolle's Theorem was introduced in Unit AB2, Section 3.

Theorem 2.1 Taylor's Theorem

Let the function f be $(n+1)$-times differentiable on an open interval containing the points a and x. Then

$$f(x) = f(a) + f'(a)(x-a) + \cdots + \frac{f^{(n)}(a)}{n!}(x-a)^n + R_n(x),$$

where

$$R_n(x) = \frac{f^{(n+1)}(c)}{(n+1)!}(x-a)^{n+1},$$

for some c between a and x.

Proof   In the proof we assume that $x > a$; the proof for $x < a$ is similar.

If you are short of time, omit this proof.

We consider the function

$$h(t) = f(t) - T_n(t) - A(t-a)^{n+1}, \tag{2.2}$$

where T_n is the Taylor polynomial of degree n at a for f, and A is a constant chosen so that

$$h(x) = 0. \tag{2.3}$$

Now, by the definition of T_n,

$$f(a) = T_n(a), \quad f'(a) = T_n'(a), \quad \ldots, \quad f^{(n)}(a) = T_n^{(n)}(a),$$

so

$$h(a) = 0, \quad h'(a) = 0, \quad \ldots, \quad h^{(n)}(a) = 0.$$

Thus the function h is continuous and differentiable on an open interval containing a and x, and $h(a) = 0 = h(x)$. So, by Rolle's Theorem applied to h on the interval $[a, x]$, there is a number c_1 between a and x for which

$$h'(c_1) = 0.$$

Now, the function h' is continuous and differentiable on I, and $h'(a) = 0 = h'(c_1)$. Hence, by Rolle's Theorem applied to h' on the interval $[a, c_1]$, there is a number c_2 between a and c_1 for which

$$h''(c_2) = 0.$$

Applying Rolle's Theorem to the functions

$$h'', h^{(3)}, \ldots, h^{(n)},$$

in turn, on the intervals

$$[a, c_2], [a, c_3], \ldots, [a, c_n], \quad \text{where } c_2 > c_3 > \cdots > c_n > a,$$

we deduce that there is a number c between a and c_n for which

$$h^{(n+1)}(c) = 0. \tag{2.4}$$

By repeatedly differentiating equation (2.2), we obtain

$$h^{(n+1)}(t) = f^{(n+1)}(t) - A(n+1)!. \qquad (2.5) \quad \text{Note that } T_n^{(n+1)}(t) = 0.$$

From equations (2.4) and (2.5), we deduce that

$$f^{(n+1)}(c) - A(n+1)! = 0, \quad \text{so} \quad A = \frac{f^{(n+1)}(c)}{(n+1)!}. \qquad (2.6)$$

Finally, it follows from equations (2.2), (2.3) and (2.6) that

$$f(x) = T_n(x) + A(x-a)^{n+1} = T_n(x) + \frac{f^{(n+1)}(c)}{(n+1)!}(x-a)^{n+1},$$

as required.   ■

The form of the remainder $R_n(x)$ given in Theorem 2.1 is actually due to Lagrange. There are other forms, due to Taylor and Cauchy, and also a neat formula which can be derived by repeated integration by parts:

$$R_n(x) = \frac{1}{n!} \int_a^x (x-t)^n f^{(n+1)}(t) \, dt.$$

Note that this form of the remainder does not involve any 'unknown numbers'.

Further exercises

Exercise 2.4   By applying Taylor's Theorem with $n = 2$ to the function $f(x) = \sin x$ at $a = \pi/4$, prove that, for $x \neq \pi/4$,

$$\sin x = \frac{1}{\sqrt{2}} + \frac{1}{\sqrt{2}}\left(x - \frac{\pi}{4}\right) - \frac{1}{2\sqrt{2}}\left(x - \frac{\pi}{4}\right)^2 - \frac{\cos c}{6}\left(x - \frac{\pi}{4}\right)^3,$$

where c lies between $\pi/4$ and x.

Exercise 2.5   Find the Taylor polynomial $T_4(x)$ at 0 for the function $f(x) = \sinh x$, and use your answer to calculate $\sinh(0.2)$ to four decimal places.

Exercise 2.6

(a) Find the Taylor polynomial $T_3(x)$ at 2 for the function $f(x) = x/(x+3)$.

(b) Show that $T_3(x)$ approximates $f(x)$ to within 6×10^{-5} on the interval $\left[2, \frac{5}{2}\right]$.

3   Convergence of power series

After working through this section, you should be able to:

(a) state the Radius of Convergence Theorem;

(b) determine the *radius of convergence* and the *interval of convergence* of certain power series.

3.1 Radius of convergence

Let $a \in \mathbb{R}$, $x \in \mathbb{R}$ and $a_n \in \mathbb{R}$, $n = 0, 1, 2, \ldots$. Then the expression

$$\sum_{n=0}^{\infty} a_n(x - a)^n = a_0 + a_1(x - a) + a_2(x - a)^2 + \cdots$$

is called a **power series about** a in x, with **coefficients** a_n. We call a the **centre** of the power series. In Section 2 you saw that certain standard functions can be expressed as the sum functions of their Taylor series; for example,

Here we think of a as a constant and x as a variable.

$$\frac{1}{1 - x} = \sum_{n=0}^{\infty} x^n, \quad \text{for } |x| < 1,$$

and

$$\log_e(1 + x) = \sum_{n=1}^{\infty} \frac{(-1)^{n+1} x^n}{n}, \quad \text{for } -1 < x \le 1,$$

and both these series are power series about 0 in x. All such Taylor series are examples of power series.

On the other hand, we can consider power series in their own right and use these to *define* functions. For example, we saw earlier that we could have defined the exponential function by the formula

See Subsection 2.2, remark 2.

$$e^x = \sum_{n=0}^{\infty} \frac{x^n}{n!} \quad (x \in \mathbb{R}).$$

In each of the above examples (where $a = 0$), the power series converges on an interval with centre a. This property is true for all power series.

Another example is the Bessel function

$$J_0(x) = \sum_{n=0}^{\infty} \frac{(-1)^n (x/2)^{2n}}{(n!)^2},$$

which arises in connection with the vibration of a circular drum.

Theorem 3.1   Radius of Convergence Theorem

For a given power series $\displaystyle\sum_{n=0}^{\infty} a_n(x - a)^n$, exactly one of the following possibilities occurs.

The proof of this theorem is in Subsection 3.2.

(a) The series converges only for $x = a$.

(b) The series converges for all x.

(c) There is a number $R > 0$ such that

$$\sum_{n=0}^{\infty} a_n(x - a)^n \text{ converges if } |x - a| < R$$

and

$$\sum_{n=0}^{\infty} a_n(x - a)^n \text{ diverges if } |x - a| > R.$$

diverges	converges	diverges
$a - R$ $\quad a$	$a + R$	

For example,

(a) $\displaystyle\sum_{n=0}^{\infty} n!\, x^n$ converges only for $x = 0$;

(b) $\displaystyle\sum_{n=0}^{\infty} \frac{x^n}{n!}$ converges for all x;

(c) $\displaystyle\sum_{n=0}^{\infty} x^n$ converges if $|x| < 1$ and diverges if $|x| > 1$, so $R = 1$.

The positive number R in Theorem 3.1(c) is called the **radius of convergence** of the power series because the power series converges at those points whose distance from the centre a is less than R, and diverges at those points whose distance from a is greater than R. We extend this definition to the cases of Theorem 3.1(a) and (b) by writing

$R = 0$ if the power series converges only for $x = a$,

and

$R = \infty$ if the power series converges for all x.

Theorem 3.1(c) makes no assertion about the behaviour of the power series at the endpoints of the interval $(a - R, a + R)$; in fact, a power series may converge at both endpoints, neither endpoint or exactly one endpoint.

The **interval of convergence** of the power series is the interval $(a - R, a + R)$, together with any endpoints of this interval at which the power series converges.

The following diagram illustrates the various possible types of interval of convergence of $\displaystyle\sum_{n=0}^{\infty} a_n(x - a)^n$.

Theorem 3.1 tells us that each power series has a radius of convergence R, but it does not tell us how to find R. However, a power series is a particular type of series, so the convergence tests for series can be applied.

We can find the radius of convergence of many power series by using the following version of the Ratio Test.

Ratio Test   Suppose that $\displaystyle\sum_{n=0}^{\infty} a_n(x - a)^n$ is a power series with radius of convergence R, and

$$\left| \frac{a_{n+1}}{a_n} \right| \to L \text{ as } n \to \infty.$$

(a) If L is ∞, then $R = 0$.
(b) If $L = 0$, then $R = \infty$.
(c) If $L > 0$, then $R = 1/L$.

The series $\displaystyle\sum_{n=0}^{\infty} n!\, x^n$ diverges for $x \neq 0$, by the Ratio Test; see Unit AA3, Section 2.

Here R is used as a symbol, not a real number.

See Example 3.2.

See Unit AA3.

The proof of this test is in Subsection 3.2.

Example 3.1   Determine the radius of convergence of each of the following power series.

(a) $\displaystyle\sum_{n=0}^{\infty} \frac{(x+2)^n}{n!}$ (b) $\displaystyle\sum_{n=0}^{\infty} \frac{n^n(x-1)^n}{n!}$

Solution

(a) Here $a_n = 1/n!$, for $n = 0, 1, 2, \ldots$, so

$$\left|\frac{a_{n+1}}{a_n}\right| = \frac{1}{(n+1)!} \times \frac{n!}{1} = \frac{1}{n+1} \to 0 \text{ as } n \to \infty.$$

Hence, by the Ratio Test for power series, $R = \infty$; that is,

$$\sum_{n=1}^{\infty} \frac{(x+2)^n}{n!} \text{ converges for all } x.$$

(b) Here $a_n = n^n/n!$, for $n = 0, 1, 2, \ldots$, so

$$\left|\frac{a_{n+1}}{a_n}\right| = \frac{(n+1)^{n+1}}{(n+1)!} \times \frac{n!}{n^n}$$

$$= \frac{(n+1)^n}{n^n} = \left(1 + \frac{1}{n}\right)^n \to e \text{ as } n \to \infty.$$

See Unit AA2, Section 5.

Hence, by the Ratio Test, the radius of convergence is $R = 1/e$. ∎

Thus this power series converges for
$$|x - 1| < 1/e,$$
and diverges for
$$|x - 1| > 1/e.$$

Exercise 3.1   Determine the radius of convergence of each of the following power series.

(a) $\displaystyle\sum_{n=0}^{\infty}(2^n + 4^n)x^n$ (b) $\displaystyle\sum_{n=1}^{\infty} \frac{(n!)^2}{(2n)!}x^n$

(c) $\displaystyle\sum_{n=0}^{\infty}(n + 2^{-n})(x-1)^n$ (d) $\displaystyle\sum_{n=1}^{\infty} n^n x^n$

Exercise 3.2   Determine the radius of convergence of the power series

$$1 + \alpha x + \frac{\alpha(\alpha-1)}{2!}x^2 + \cdots = \sum_{n=0}^{\infty} \frac{\alpha(\alpha-1)\cdots(\alpha-n+1)}{n!}x^n,$$

where $\alpha \neq 0, 1, 2, \ldots$.

This power series plays an important role in Section 4. If $\alpha \in \{0, 1, 2, \ldots\}$, then the power series has only finitely many non-zero terms.

The Ratio Test gives an open interval on which a power series converges. To determine the interval of convergence of a power series with finite non-zero radius of convergence, we need to use other tests to find the behaviour at the interval endpoints.

Strategy 3.1   To find the interval of convergence of $\displaystyle\sum_{n=0}^{\infty} a_n(x-a)^n$.

1. Use the Ratio Test for power series to find the radius of convergence R.

2. Use other tests for series to determine the behaviour of the power series at the endpoints of the interval $(a - R, a + R)$.

Example 3.2   Determine the interval of convergence of each of the following power series.

In each of these power series the coefficient $a_0 = 0$.

(a) $\displaystyle\sum_{n=1}^{\infty} x^n$ (b) $\displaystyle\sum_{n=1}^{\infty} \frac{x^n}{n}$ (c) $\displaystyle\sum_{n=1}^{\infty} \frac{(x-3)^n}{2^n n^2}$

Solution   In each case, we apply Strategy 3.1.

(a) Here $a_n = 1$, for $n = 1, 2, \ldots$.

  1. Since

$$\left| \frac{a_{n+1}}{a_n} \right| = 1, \quad \text{for } n = 1, 2, \ldots,$$

     we have $R = 1$, by the Ratio Test. Thus (by the Radius of Convergence Theorem) this power series

      converges for $-1 < x < 1$,

      diverges for $x > 1$ and $x < -1$.

  2. If $x = 1$, then the power series is

$$\sum_{n=1}^{\infty} 1^n, \quad \text{which is divergent,}$$

     by the Non-null Test.

See Unit AA3, Section 1.

     If $x = -1$, then the power series is

$$\sum_{n=1}^{\infty} (-1)^n, \quad \text{which is divergent,}$$

     by the Non-null Test.

Hence the interval of convergence is $(-1, 1)$.

(b) Here $a_n = 1/n$, for $n = 1, 2, \ldots$.

  1. Since

$$\left| \frac{a_{n+1}}{a_n} \right| = \frac{1}{n+1} \times \frac{n}{1} = \frac{1}{1 + 1/n} \to 1 \ \text{ as } n \to \infty,$$

     we have $R = 1$, by the Ratio Test. Thus this power series

      converges for $-1 < x < 1$,

      diverges for $x > 1$ and $x < -1$.

  2. If $x = 1$, then the power series is

$$\sum_{n=1}^{\infty} \frac{1}{n}, \quad \text{which is a basic divergent series.}$$

See Unit AA3, Section 2.

     If $x = -1$, then the power series is

$$\sum_{n=1}^{\infty} \frac{(-1)^n}{n}, \quad \text{which is convergent,}$$

     by the Alternating Test.

See Unit AA3, Section 3.

Hence the interval of convergence is $[-1, 1)$.

(c) Here $a_n = 1/(2^n n^2)$, for $n = 1, 2, \ldots$.

  1. Since

$$\left| \frac{a_{n+1}}{a_n} \right| = \frac{1}{2^{n+1}(n+1)^2} \times \frac{2^n n^2}{1} = \frac{1}{2(1 + 1/n)^2} \to \frac{1}{2} \ \text{ as } n \to \infty,$$

we have $R = 2$, by the Ratio Test. Since $a = 3$, this power series

converges for $1 < x < 5$,

diverges for $x > 5$ and $x < 1$.

We have
$$|x - 3| < 2 \Leftrightarrow -2 < x - 3 < 2$$
$$\Leftrightarrow 1 < x < 5.$$

2. If $x = 5$, then the power series is

$$\sum_{n=1}^{\infty} \frac{1}{2^n n^2}(5 - 3)^n = \sum_{n=1}^{\infty} \frac{1}{n^2}, \quad \text{which is a basic convergent series.}$$

If $x = 1$, then the power series is

$$\sum_{n=1}^{\infty} \frac{1}{2^n n^2}(1 - 3)^n = \sum_{n=1}^{\infty} \frac{(-1)^n}{n^2}, \quad \text{which is convergent,}$$

by the Absolute Convergence Test.

See Unit AA3, Section 3.

Hence the interval of convergence is $[1, 5]$. ■

Exercise 3.3   Determine the interval of convergence of each of the following power series.

(a) $\displaystyle\sum_{n=1}^{\infty} n x^n$ (b) $\displaystyle\sum_{n=1}^{\infty} \frac{(-1)^n}{n 3^n}(x - 5)^n$

3.2 Proofs (optional)

To prove the Radius of Convergence Theorem, we need the following preliminary result.

Lemma 3.1   If the power series $\displaystyle\sum_{n=0}^{\infty} a_n x^n$ converges for some $x_0 \neq 0$, then it is absolutely convergent on the interval $(-|x_0|, |x_0|)$.

The following diagram illustrates the statement of the lemma in the two possible cases $x_0 > 0$ and $x_0 < 0$.

In what follows, we often use without reference the fact that an absolutely convergent series is convergent. This follows by the Absolute Convergence Test; see Unit AA3, Section 3.

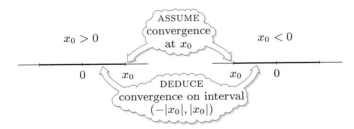

Proof   First we write $r = |x_0|$. Since the series $\displaystyle\sum_{n=0}^{\infty} a_n x_0^n$ is convergent,

See Unit AA3, Section 1.

the sequence $\{a_n x_0^n\}$ is null and hence there is a number K such that

$$|a_n| r^n = |a_n x_0^n| \leq K, \quad \text{for } n = 0, 1, 2, \dots. \tag{3.1}$$

See Unit AA2, Theorem 4.1.

Suppose that $|x| < r$. To prove that $\displaystyle\sum_{n=0}^{\infty} a_n x^n$ is absolutely convergent, we write

$$a_n x^n = a_n r^n \left(\frac{x}{r}\right)^n.$$

Then, by inequality (3.1),

$$|a_n x^n| = |a_n| r^n \left| \frac{x}{r} \right|^n \le K \left| \frac{x}{r} \right|^n .$$

Since $|x| < r$, we have $|x|/r < 1$, so the geometric series

$$\sum_{n=0}^{\infty} K \left(\frac{|x|}{r} \right)^n \text{ is convergent.}$$

Hence, by the Comparison Test, $\sum_{n=0}^{\infty} |a_n x^n|$ is convergent, as required. ∎   See Unit AA3, Section 2.

We can now prove that every power series has a radius of convergence.

Theorem 3.1 Radius of Convergence Theorem

For a given power series $\sum_{n=0}^{\infty} a_n (x - a)^n$, exactly one of the following possibilities occurs.

(a) The series converges only for $x = a$.

(b) The series converges for all x.

(c) There is a number $R > 0$ such that

$$\sum_{n=0}^{\infty} a_n (x - a)^n \text{ converges if } |x - a| < R$$

and

$$\sum_{n=0}^{\infty} a_n (x - a)^n \text{ diverges if } |x - a| > R.$$

---

diverges   converges   diverges

$a - R \quad a \quad a + R$

Proof   We give the proof only in the case $a = 0$.   The proof of the general case is similar.

Let

$$E = \{ x \in \mathbb{R} : \sum_{n=0}^{\infty} a_n x^n \text{ is convergent} \}.$$

If $E = \{0\}$, then possibility (a) holds.

If E is unbounded, then for every $x \in \mathbb{R}$ there exists $x_0 \in E$ such that $|x| < |x_0|$. Thus, the series $\sum_{n=0}^{\infty} a_n x^n$ is absolutely convergent, by Lemma 3.1. Hence possibility (b) holds.

Otherwise, the set E is bounded and contains a point $x_0 \ne 0$. Then $(-|x_0|, |x_0|) \subseteq E$, by Lemma 3.1, so $\sup E \ge |x_0|$. We define $R = \sup E$.

If $|x| < R$, then we can find $x_1 \in E$ such that $|x| < x_1$. Thus, by Lemma 3.1, the series $\sum_{n=0}^{\infty} a_n x^n$ is absolutely convergent.

$0 \qquad |x| \qquad x_1 \quad R = \sup E$

If $|x| > R$, then we can find $x_2 > R$ such that $|x| > x_2$, so $\sum_{n=0}^{\infty} a_n x^n$ is divergent (since if $\sum_{n=0}^{\infty} a_n x^n$ is convergent, then $\sum_{n=0}^{\infty} a_n x_2^n$ is convergent, by Lemma 3.1). Hence possibility (c) holds.

$0 \qquad R = \sup E \quad x_2 \quad |x|$

This completes the proof. ∎

Remark   The above proof shows that a power series is not just convergent but *absolutely* convergent at each interior point of its interval of convergence.

Ratio Test   Suppose that $\sum_{n=0}^{\infty} a_n(x-a)^n$ is a power series with radius of convergence R, and

$$\left| \frac{a_{n+1}}{a_n} \right| \to L \ \text{ as } n \to \infty. \tag{3.2}$$

(a) If L is ∞, then $R = 0$.
(b) If $L = 0$, then $R = \infty$.
(c) If $L > 0$, then $R = 1/L$.

Proof   We assume again that $a = 0$.

(a) Suppose that statement (3.2) holds, where L is ∞. Then, for $x \neq 0$,

$$\frac{|a_{n+1}x^{n+1}|}{|a_n x^n|} = \left| \frac{a_{n+1}}{a_n} \right| |x| \to \infty \ \text{ as } n \to \infty,$$

so $\sum_{n=0}^{\infty} |a_n x^n|$ is divergent, by the Ratio Test (for series).

See Unit AA3, Section 2.

Thus $R = 0$.

(b) Suppose that statement (3.2) holds, with $L = 0$. Then, for $x \neq 0$,

$$\frac{|a_{n+1}x^{n+1}|}{|a_n x^n|} = \left| \frac{a_{n+1}}{a_n} \right| |x| \to 0 \times |x| = 0 < 1 \ \text{ as } n \to \infty,$$

so $\sum_{n=0}^{\infty} |a_n x^n|$ is convergent, by the Ratio Test (for series).

Thus $R = \infty$.

(c) Suppose that statement (3.2) holds, with $L > 0$.

If $|x| > 1/L$, then

$$\frac{|a_{n+1}x^{n+1}|}{|a_n x^n|} = \left| \frac{a_{n+1}}{a_n} \right| |x| \to L|x| > 1 \ \text{ as } n \to \infty,$$

so $\sum_{n=0}^{\infty} |a_n x^n|$ is divergent, by the Ratio Test (for series).

However, if $0 < |x| < 1/L$, then

$$\frac{|a_{n+1}x^{n+1}|}{|a_n x^n|} = \left| \frac{a_{n+1}}{a_n} \right| |x| \to L|x| < 1 \ \text{ as } n \to \infty,$$

so $\sum_{n=0}^{\infty} |a_n x^n|$ is convergent, by the Ratio Test (for series).

Thus $R = 1/L$.

This completes the proof.   ∎

Further exercises

Exercise 3.4   Determine the radius of convergence of each of the following power series.

(a) $\displaystyle\sum_{n=0}^{\infty} \frac{(3n)!}{(n!)^2}(x+2)^n$ (b) $\displaystyle\sum_{n=1}^{\infty} \frac{n!}{n^n}(x-5)^n$ (c) $\displaystyle\sum_{n=0}^{\infty} \frac{x^n}{(n+1)^n}$

Exercise 3.5   Determine the interval of convergence of each of the following power series.

(a) $\displaystyle\sum_{n=0}^{\infty} \frac{2^n}{n!}x^n$ (b) $\displaystyle\sum_{n=1}^{\infty} \frac{2^n}{n}(x+1)^n$

4   Manipulating power series

After working through this section, you should be able to:

(a) state and use the Combination Rules, Product Rule, Differentiation Rule and Integration Rule for power series;
(b) state and use the General Binomial Theorem;
(c) understand and use the Identity Theorem for power series.

4.1 Operations on power series

You have already seen the following Taylor series at 0:

$$\frac{1}{1-x} = 1 + x + x^2 + \cdots = \sum_{n=0}^{\infty} x^n, \quad \text{for } |x| < 1. \tag{4.1}$$

This power series has radius of convergence 1.

We can obtain the sum functions for further power series by using various operations on known power series. For example, since $|-x| < 1$ if and only if $|x| < 1$, we deduce from equation (4.1) that

$$\frac{1}{1+x} = 1 - x + x^2 - \cdots = \sum_{n=0}^{\infty} (-1)^n x^n, \quad \text{for } |x| < 1,$$

and this power series also has radius of convergence 1.

Similarly, since $|3x^2| < 1$ if and only if $|x| < 1/\sqrt{3}$, we deduce from equation (4.1) that

$$\frac{1}{1-3x^2} = 1 + 3x^2 + (3x^2)^2 + (3x^2)^3 + \cdots$$
$$= \sum_{n=0}^{\infty} 3^n x^{2n}, \quad \text{for } |x| < 1/\sqrt{3},$$

and this power series has radius of convergence $1/\sqrt{3}$.

In the audio section we discuss various ways to obtain power series representations for new functions. It is natural to ask if these power series are always the Taylor series of the corresponding functions, and this turns out to be true. At the end of the audio we prove that a function has at   See Frame 14.

most one power series representation near any point a, so any power series representation that we find must be the Taylor series at a.

During the audio we prove a result which gives the Taylor series at 0 for the function $f(x) = (1+x)^\alpha$, where $\alpha \in \mathbb{R}$. We show that

$$(1+x)^\alpha = \sum_{n=0}^{\infty} \binom{\alpha}{n} x^n, \quad \text{for } |x| < 1,$$

where the coefficients are the **generalised binomial coefficients** defined as follows:

$$\binom{\alpha}{0} = 1, \quad \binom{\alpha}{n} = \frac{\alpha(\alpha-1)(\alpha-2)\cdots(\alpha-n+1)}{n!}, \quad n \in \mathbb{N}.$$

For example,

$$\binom{-\frac{1}{2}}{n} = \frac{(-\frac{1}{2})(-\frac{3}{2})(-\frac{5}{2})\cdots(-\frac{1}{2}-n+1)}{n!}$$

$$= (-1)^n \frac{1 \cdot 3 \cdot 5 \cdot \cdots \cdot (2n-1)}{2^n n!}. \tag{4.2}$$

In the proof we use the following identity involving these coefficients.

In Exercise 3.2 you saw that this power series has radius of convergence 1, for $\alpha \neq 0, 1, 2, \ldots$.

The usual binomial coefficients are

$$\binom{n}{k} = \frac{n!}{k!(n-k)!}$$

$$= \frac{n(n-1)\cdots(n-k+1)}{k!},$$

where n and k are integers such that $0 \le k \le n$.

See Frame 13.

Lemma 4.1 For all $\alpha \in \mathbb{R}$ and $|x| < 1$,

$$(1+x)\sum_{n=1}^{\infty} n\binom{\alpha}{n} x^{n-1} = \sum_{n=0}^{\infty} c_n x^n,$$

where

$$c_n = n\binom{\alpha}{n} + (n+1)\binom{\alpha}{n+1} = \alpha\binom{\alpha}{n}.$$

Proof   We have

$$(1+x)\sum_{n=1}^{\infty} n\binom{\alpha}{n} x^{n-1} = \sum_{n=1}^{\infty} n\binom{\alpha}{n} x^{n-1} + \sum_{n=1}^{\infty} n\binom{\alpha}{n} x^n$$

$$= \sum_{n=0}^{\infty} (n+1)\binom{\alpha}{n+1} x^n + \sum_{n=0}^{\infty} n\binom{\alpha}{n} x^n$$

$$= \sum_{n=0}^{\infty} c_n x^n,$$

where

$$c_n = n\binom{\alpha}{n} + (n+1)\binom{\alpha}{n+1}$$

$$= n\binom{\alpha}{n} + (n+1)\frac{\alpha(\alpha-1)\cdots(\alpha-n+1)(\alpha-n)}{(n+1)!}$$

$$= n\binom{\alpha}{n} + (\alpha-n)\binom{\alpha}{n} = \alpha\binom{\alpha}{n}. \quad \blacksquare$$

Listen to the audio as you work through the frames.

Audio

27

1. Taylor polynomials and Taylor series at a for f

Taylor polynomial of degree n at a for f

$$T_n(x) = a_0 + a_1(x-a) + \cdots + a_n(x-a)^n, \text{ where } a_k = \frac{f^{(k)}(a)}{k!}.$$

Taylor's Theorem

$$f(x) = T_n(x) + R_n(x), \quad R_n(x) = \frac{f^{(n+1)}(c)}{(n+1)!}(x-a)^{n+1}.$$

> $T_n(x) \longrightarrow f(x)$
> $\Updownarrow$
> $R_n(x) \longrightarrow 0$

Taylor series

$$f(x) = a_0 + a_1(x-a) + \cdots + a_n(x-a)^n + \cdots = \sum_{n=0}^{\infty} a_n(x-a)^n.$$

2. What is the Taylor series at 0 for cosh?

$$e^x = 1 + x + \frac{x^2}{2!} + \cdots + \frac{x^n}{n!} + \cdots,$$

$$e^{-x} = 1 - x + \frac{x^2}{2!} - \cdots + (-1)^n \frac{x^n}{n!} + \cdots$$

> Can we add?

$$e^x + e^{-x} = 2 + 2\frac{x^2}{2!} + 2\frac{x^4}{4!} + \cdots + 2\frac{x^{2n}}{(2n)!} + \cdots \quad \text{for } x \in \mathbb{R}.$$

> Can we multiply by $\frac{1}{2}$?

> $\cosh x = \frac{1}{2}(e^x + e^{-x})$

$$\cosh x = 1 + \frac{x^2}{2!} + \frac{x^4}{4!} + \cdots + \frac{x^{2n}}{(2n)!} + \cdots \quad \text{for } x \in \mathbb{R}.$$

3. Combining power series

> Apply Combination Rules for series

Combination Rules   If

$$f(x) = \sum_{n=0}^{\infty} a_n(x-a)^n, \text{ for } |x-a| < R,$$

$$g(x) = \sum_{n=0}^{\infty} b_n(x-a)^n, \text{ for } |x-a| < R',$$

then:

Sum Rule

$$(f+g)(x) = \sum_{n=0}^{\infty} (a_n + b_n)(x-a)^n, \text{ for } |x-a| < r,$$

$$\text{where } r = \min\{R, R'\};$$

Multiple Rule   for $\lambda \in \mathbb{R}$,

$$(\lambda f)(x) = \sum_{n=0}^{\infty} \lambda a_n(x-a)^n, \text{ for } |x-a| < R.$$

> radius of convergence may be > r

4. Exercise 4.1

Find the Taylor series at 0 for:

(a) $f(x) = \sinh x$;

(b) $\log_e(1-x) + 2(1-x)^{-1}$.

5. What is the Taylor series at 0 for f(x) = $\frac{1+x}{1-x}$?

Can we multiply?

$$(1-x)^{-1} = 1 + x + x^2 + \dots + x^n + \dots, \text{ for } |x| < 1$$

$$(1+x) \times (1-x)^{-1} = (1 + x + x^2 + \dots + x^n + \dots)$$
$$+ (x + x^2 + \dots + x^n + \dots)$$
$$= 1 + 2x + 2x^2 + \dots + 2x^n + \dots .$$

6. Multiplying power series

Product Rule If

$f(x) = a_0 + a_1(x-a) + \dots + a_n(x-a)^n + \dots$ for $|x-a| < R$,

$g(x) = b_0 + b_1(x-a) + \dots + b_n(x-a)^n + \dots$ for $|x-a| < R'$,

and $r = \min\{R, R'\}$, then

$(fg)(x) = c_0 + c_1(x-a) + \dots + c_n(x-a)^n + \dots$ for $|x-a| < r$,

where $c_0 = a_0 b_0$, $\quad c_1 = a_0 b_1 + a_1 b_0, \dots$,

and $\quad c_n = a_0 b_n + a_1 b_{n-1} + \dots + a_{n-1} b_1 + a_n b_0$.

radius of convergence may be > r

7. What is the Taylor series at 0 for f(x) = $\frac{1+x}{(1-x)^2}$?

Product Rule $|x| < 1$

$$\frac{1+x}{(1-x)^2} = \frac{1+x}{1-x} \times \frac{1}{1-x}$$

$$= (1 + 2x + 2x^2 + \dots + 2x^n + \dots)(1 + x + x^2 + \dots + x^n + \dots)$$

$$= \sum_{n=0}^{\infty} c_n x^n, \quad \text{where}$$

$c_0 = \boxed{1}$, $c_1 = \boxed{3}$, $c_2 = \boxed{5}$, ..., $c_n = \boxed{2n+1}$

for $n = 0, 1, 2, \dots$

Hence

$$\frac{1+x}{(1-x)^2} = \boxed{1} + \boxed{3}\,x + \boxed{5}\,x^2 + \dots + \boxed{2n+1}\,x^n + \dots$$

for $|x| < 1$.

8. Exercise 4.2

Find the Taylor series at 0 for :

(a) $f(x) = (1+x) \log_e (1+x)$;

(b) $f(x) = \dfrac{1+x}{(1-x)^3}$.

29

9. Differentiating and integrating power series

Can we differentiate?

$$\cosh x = 1 + \frac{x^2}{2!} + \frac{x^4}{4!} + \cdots + \frac{x^{2n}}{(2n)!} + \cdots$$

Can we integrate?

$$\sinh x = x + \frac{x^3}{3!} + \cdots + \frac{x^{2n-1}}{(2n-1)!} + \cdots$$

constant of $\int = \cosh 0 = 1$

10. Differentiation and Integration Rules (at 0)

Let $f(x) = \sum_{n=0}^{\infty} a_n x^n$,   for $|x| < R$,

Differentiation Rule

$$f'(x) = \sum_{n=1}^{\infty} n a_n x^{n-1},   \text{for } |x| < R,$$

Integration Rule

$$\int f(x)\, dx = \sum_{n=0}^{\infty} \frac{a_n}{n+1} x^{n+1} + \text{constant},   \text{for } |x| < R,$$

(to find constant, put $x = 0$)

all 3 series have same R, but may behave differently at R, − R

11. Taylor series at 0 for $\tan^{-1}$

$$\frac{d}{dx} \tan^{-1} x = \frac{1}{1+x^2}$$ for $|x| < 1$.

Geometric series :

$$\frac{1}{1+x^2} = 1 - x^2 + x^4 - \cdots,$$

By the Integration Rule,

$$\tan^{-1} x = x - \frac{x^3}{3} + \frac{x^5}{5} - \cdots + \text{constant},   \text{for } |x| < 1.$$

$\tan^{-1} 0 = 0 \Rightarrow \text{constant} = 0$

$$= x - \frac{x^3}{3} + \frac{x^5}{5} - \cdots,   \text{for } |x| < 1,$$

also valid when $x = 1, -1$

12. Exercise 4.3

Find the Taylor series at 0 for :

(a) $f(x) = (1-x)^{-2}$;

(b) $f(x) = (1-x)^{-3}$;

(c) $f(x) = \tanh^{-1} x$.

14. Theorem 4.2 Identity Theorem

If $\displaystyle\sum_{n=0}^{\infty} a_n (x-a)^n = \sum_{n=0}^{\infty} b_n (x-a)^n$,   for $|x| < R$,

then $a_n = b_n$,   for $n = 0, 1, \ldots$.

Proof   Let $\displaystyle f(x) = \sum_{n=0}^{\infty} a_n (x-a)^n$,

$$g(x) = \sum_{n=0}^{\infty} b_n (x-a)^n \, ;$$

then $\displaystyle a_n = \frac{f^{(n)}(a)}{n!} = \frac{g^{(n)}(a)}{n!} = b_n$.

differentiate each series n times and put x = a

ANY METHOD GIVES SAME a_n

15. Summary of techniques

- use $\displaystyle f(x) = \sum_{n=0}^{\infty} a_n (x-a)^n$, $a_n = \dfrac{f^{(n)}(a)}{n!}$ Frame 1

- use Combination Rules   Frame 3

- use Product Rule   Frame 6

- use Differentiation and Integration Rules   Frame 10

- use General Binomial Theorem   Frame 13

13. Theorem 4.1 General Binomial Theorem

$$(1+x)^\alpha = \sum_{n=0}^{\infty} \binom{\alpha}{n} x^n, \;\; \alpha \in \mathbb{R}, \;\; \text{for } |x| < 1.$$

where $\displaystyle \binom{\alpha}{n} = \frac{\alpha(\alpha-1)\cdots(\alpha-n+1)}{n!}$

WANT g(x)=1

Proof   Let $\displaystyle f(x) = \sum_{n=0}^{\infty} \binom{\alpha}{n} x^n$,

$$g(x) = f(x)(1+x)^{-\alpha} \, ;$$

then $g'(x) = f'(x)(1+x)^{-\alpha} - \alpha f(x)(1+x)^{-\alpha-1}$

$$= \big[(1+x)f'(x) - \alpha f(x)\big](1+x)^{-\alpha-1}.$$

Now $\displaystyle (1+x)f'(x) = (1+x)\sum_{n=1}^{\infty} n\binom{\alpha}{n} x^{n-1} = \sum_{n=0}^{\infty} c_n x^n$,

where $\displaystyle c_n = n\binom{\alpha}{n} + (n+1)\binom{\alpha}{n+1} = \alpha\binom{\alpha}{n}$.

Hence $\big[(1+x)f'(x) - \alpha f(x)\big] = 0$, so $g'(x) = 0$.

Thus $g(x) = constant = g(0) = f(0) = 1$, so

$$f(x) = (1+x)^\alpha.$$

31

Post-audio exercises

Exercise 4.4 Determine the Taylor series at 0 for each of the following functions; in each case, indicate the general term and state a range of validity for the series.

(a) $f(x) = \sinh x + \sin x$ (b) $f(x) = 1/(1 + 2x^2)$

Exercise 4.5 Determine the first three non-zero terms in the Taylor series at 0 for the function $f(x) = e^x(1-x)^{-2}$, and state a range of validity for the series.

Hint: Use the solution to Exercise 4.3(a).

Exercise 4.6 Determine the Taylor series at 0 for the function $f(x) = e^{-x^2}$. Deduce that

$$\int_0^1 e^{-x^2}\,dx = 1 - \frac{1}{3} + \frac{1}{10} - \cdots + \frac{(-1)^n}{(2n+1)n!} + \cdots.$$

Exercise 4.7

(a) Write down the Taylor series at 0 for the function $f(x) = 1/(1+x)$.

(b) Use your solution to part (a) to find the Taylor series at 0 for the function $f(x) = \log_e(1 + x)$, and state a range of validity for the series.

Exercise 4.8 Use the General Binomial Theorem to find the first three non-zero terms in the Taylor series at 0 for the function $f(x) = (1+x)^{-1/3}$.

In Exercise 4.7(b) we have finally established that the Taylor series at 0 for $\log_e(1 + x)$ is valid on the *whole* of the interval $(-1, 1]$. In Theorem 2.3(e) we proved only that it is valid on $[0, 1]$.

4.2 Proofs (optional)

The Sum and Multiple Rules for power series are special cases of the Sum and Multiple Rules for series. We now prove the Product Rule.

See Unit AA3, Section 1.

Product Rule Let

$$f(x) = \sum_{n=0}^{\infty} a_n (x - a)^n, \quad \text{for } |x - a| < R,$$

$$g(x) = \sum_{n=0}^{\infty} b_n (x - a)^n, \quad \text{for } |x - a| < R',$$

and $r = \min\{R, R'\}$. Then

$$(fg)(x) = \sum_{n=0}^{\infty} c_n (x - a)^n, \quad \text{for } |x - a| < r,$$

where

$$c_n = a_0 b_n + a_1 b_{n-1} + \cdots + a_{n-1} b_1 + a_n b_0 = \sum_{k=0}^{n} a_k b_{n-k}.$$

Proof   For simplicity, we assume that $a = 0$.

Take $n \geq 2$ and put $m = [\frac{1}{2}n]$. Then

$$\sum_{i=0}^{n} a_i x^i \times \sum_{j=0}^{n} b_j x^j = \sum_{k=0}^{n} c_k x^k + \text{the sum of those terms } a_i b_j x^{i+j}$$

$$\text{in } \sum_{i=0}^{n} a_i x^i \times \sum_{j=0}^{n} b_j x^j \text{ with } i + j > n.$$

Here, $[x]$ is the integer part of x, that is, the largest integer less than or equal to x.

Thus, by the Triangle Inequality,

$$\left| \sum_{i=0}^{n} a_i x^i \times \sum_{j=0}^{n} b_j x^j - \sum_{k=0}^{n} c_k x^k \right| \leq \text{the sum of those terms } \left| a_i b_j x^{i+j} \right|$$

$$\text{in } \sum_{i=0}^{n} |a_i x^i| \times \sum_{j=0}^{n} |b_j x^j| \text{ with } i + j > n.$$

But all the latter terms are included in the expression

$$\sum_{i=0}^{n} |a_i x^i| \times \sum_{j=0}^{n} |b_j x^j| - \sum_{i=0}^{m} |a_i x^i| \times \sum_{j=0}^{m} |b_j x^j|,$$

and the other terms in this expression are all non-negative.

Hence

$$\left| \sum_{i=0}^{n} a_i x^i \times \sum_{j=0}^{n} b_j x^j - \sum_{k=0}^{n} c_k x^k \right|$$

$$\leq \sum_{i=0}^{n} |a_i x^i| \times \sum_{j=0}^{n} |b_j x^j| - \sum_{i=0}^{m} |a_i x^i| \times \sum_{j=0}^{m} |b_j x^j|. \tag{4.3}$$

Now suppose that $|x| < r$, so the series $\sum_{i=0}^{\infty} |a_i x^i|$ and $\sum_{j=0}^{\infty} |b_j x^j|$ are both

convergent, with sums s and t, respectively. As $n \to \infty$, the right-hand side of inequality (4.3) tends to $st - st = 0$, since $m \to \infty$. Thus, by the

Limit Inequality Rule, $\sum_{k=0}^{\infty} c_k x^k$ converges, and

See the remark on page 25 after the proof of Theorem 3.1.

See Unit AA2, Section 3.

$$\sum_{k=0}^{\infty} c_k x^k = \sum_{i=0}^{\infty} a_i x^i \times \sum_{j=0}^{\infty} b_j x^j.$$

This completes the proof of the Product Rule.   ■

Differentiation Rule   The power series

$$\sum_{n=0}^{\infty} a_n (x - a)^n \quad \text{and} \quad \sum_{n=1}^{\infty} n a_n (x - a)^{n-1}$$

have the same radius of convergence, R say.

Also, $f(x) = \sum_{n=0}^{\infty} a_n (x - a)^n$ is differentiable on $(a - R, a + R)$, and

$$f'(x) = \sum_{n=1}^{\infty} n a_n (x - a)^{n-1}, \quad \text{for } |x - a| < R.$$

Proof   For simplicity, we assume again that $a = 0$.

Let the series $\sum\limits_{n=0}^{\infty} a_n x^n$ and $\sum\limits_{n=1}^{\infty} n a_n x^{n-1}$ have radii of convergence R and R', respectively. We prove that $R' = R$.

We first show that $R' \geq R$. To prove this, suppose that $|x| < R$. Now choose r such that $|x| < r < R$. Then $\sum\limits_{n=0}^{\infty} a_n r^n$ is convergent, so $\{a_n r^n\}$ is a null sequence. Thus there is a positive number K such that

$$|a_n r^n| \leq K, \quad \text{for } n = 0, 1, 2, \ldots. \tag{4.4}$$

Then

$$|n a_n x^{n-1}| = \frac{|n a_n r^n x^{n-1}|}{r^n} \leq \frac{K}{r} n \left(\frac{|x|}{r}\right)^{n-1}, \quad \text{for } n = 1, 2, \ldots, \tag{4.5}$$

by statement (4.4). Since $|x|/r < 1$, the series $\sum\limits_{n=1}^{\infty} n \left(|x|/r\right)^{n-1}$ converges.

See the solution to Exercise 3.3(a).

Therefore, by statement (4.5) and the Comparison Test, $\sum\limits_{n=1}^{\infty} |n a_n x^{n-1}|$ is convergent for all $|x| < R$. Thus $R' \geq R$.

See Unit AA3, Section 2.

Next we show that $R \geq R'$. To prove this, suppose that $|x| < R'$. Then $\sum\limits_{n=1}^{\infty} n a_n x^{n-1}$ is absolutely convergent and

$$|a_n x^n| = |n a_n x^{n-1}| \frac{|x|}{n} \leq |x| \, |n a_n x^{n-1}|, \quad \text{for } n = 1, 2, \ldots.$$

Therefore, by the Comparison Test, $\sum\limits_{n=1}^{\infty} |a_n x^n|$ is convergent for all $|x| < R'$. Thus $R \geq R'$, so we deduce that $R' = R$.

Differentiating the terms of $\sum\limits_{n=1}^{\infty} n a_n x^{n-1}$, we deduce that

$$\sum_{n=2}^{\infty} n(n-1) a_n x^{n-2} \text{ also has radius of convergence } R. \tag{4.6}$$

Let $f(x) = \sum\limits_{n=0}^{\infty} a_n x^n$. We now use statement (4.6) to prove that f' exists and has the required form on $(-R, R)$.

Take $x \in (-R, R)$, and choose r such that $|x| < r < R$. Then, for all h such that $|x + h| < r$,

$$\frac{f(x+h) - f(x)}{h} - \sum_{n=1}^{\infty} n a_n x^{n-1} = \sum_{n=2}^{\infty} a_n \frac{\left((x+h)^n - x^n - n x^{n-1} h\right)}{h}. \tag{4.7}$$

Now we apply Taylor's Theorem to the function $p(x) = x^n$ on an open interval containing x and $x + h$. We obtain

$$(x+h)^n = x^n + n x^{n-1} h + \frac{1}{2!} n(n-1) c_n^{n-2} h^2,$$

We have
$$p'(x) = n x^{n-1},$$
$$p''(x) = n(n-1) x^{n-2}.$$

where c_n lies between x and $x + h$. Then $|c_n| < r$, so

$$|(x + h)^n - x^n - nx^{n-1}h| \leq \tfrac{1}{2}n(n-1)r^{n-2}|h|^2. \tag{4.8}$$

By statements (4.7) and (4.8), and the Triangle Inequality,

$$\left| \frac{f(x+h) - f(x)}{h} - \sum_{n=1}^{\infty} na_n x^{n-1} \right| \leq \tfrac{1}{2}|h| \sum_{n=2}^{\infty} n(n-1)|a_n|r^{n-2}. \tag{4.9}$$

Since $r < R$, the series $\displaystyle\sum_{n=2}^{\infty} n(n-1)a_n r^{n-2}$ is absolutely convergent, by statement (4.6). Thus, by inequality (4.9) and the Limit Inequality Rule,

$$f'(x) = \lim_{h \to 0} \frac{f(x+h) - f(x)}{h} = \sum_{n=1}^{\infty} na_n x^{n-1}, \quad \text{for } |x| < R. \quad \blacksquare$$

Integration Rule   The power series

$$f(x) = \sum_{n=0}^{\infty} a_n(x-a)^n \quad \text{and} \quad F(x) = \sum_{n=0}^{\infty} \frac{a_n}{n+1}(x-a)^{n+1}$$

have the same radius of convergence, R say.

Also, if $R > 0$, then

$$\int f(x)\, dx = F(x), \quad \text{for } |x - a| < R.$$

That is, F is a primitive of f on $(a - R, a + R)$.

Proof   The two power series have the same radius of convergence, by the Differentiation Rule applied to F.

By the same rule, $F' = f$, so F is a primitive of f on $(a - R, a + R)$. $\blacksquare$

Further exercises

Exercise 4.9   Determine the Taylor series at 0 for each of the following functions; in each case, indicate the general term and state a range of validity for the series.

(a) $f(x) = \log_e\left(\dfrac{1 + 2x}{1 - 2x}\right)$ (b) $f(x) = \dfrac{\cosh x}{1 - x}$

Exercise 4.10   Determine the first three non-zero terms in the Taylor series at 0 for the function $f(x) = e^x \sin x$ and state a range of validity for the series.

Exercise 4.11

(a) Find the Taylor series at 0 for the function $f(x) = (1 - x)^{-1/2}$.

(b) Use your solution to part (a) to find the Taylor series at 0 for the function $f(x) = \sin^{-1} x$ and state a range of validity for the series.

5 Numerical estimates for π

After working through this section, you should be able to understand the role of power series in the numerical estimation of π.

One of the problems that has fascinated mathematicians for thousands of years has been how to determine accurately various important irrational numbers such as $\sqrt{2}$, π and e. In this section we discuss the estimation of π and we prove that π is irrational.

5.1 Tangent formulas

Earlier, you saw that the Taylor series at 0 for the function $\tan^{-1}$ is

$$\tan^{-1} x = x - \frac{x^3}{3} + \frac{x^5}{5} - \frac{x^7}{7} + \cdots, \quad \text{for } x \in [-1, 1];$$

See Subsection 4.1, Frame 11.

in particular, with $x = 1$,

$$\frac{\pi}{4} = 1 - \frac{1}{3} + \frac{1}{5} - \frac{1}{7} + \cdots.$$

This series is not very useful for calculating π, as its successive partial sums converge far too slowly. However, we can use the Taylor series for $\tan^{-1} x$ effectively for calculating π by choosing suitable values of x close to 0; in fact, the smaller the value of x, the faster the series converges, so the fewer the terms needed to calculate its sum to a given accuracy.

To obtain series that are more effective for calculating π, we can use the addition formula for $\tan^{-1}$:

$$\tan^{-1} x + \tan^{-1} y = \tan^{-1}\left(\frac{x+y}{1-xy}\right), \quad \text{for } x, y \in \mathbb{R},$$

See Unit AA4, Exercise 4.8.

provided that $\tan^{-1} x + \tan^{-1} y$ lies in $(-\frac{1}{2}\pi, \frac{1}{2}\pi)$. For example, applying this formula with $x = \frac{1}{2}$ and $y = \frac{1}{3}$, we obtain

$$\tan^{-1}\left(\tfrac{1}{2}\right) + \tan^{-1}\left(\tfrac{1}{3}\right) = \pi/4.$$

Similar applications of the addition formula give:

$$4\tan^{-1}\left(\tfrac{1}{5}\right) - \tan^{-1}\left(\tfrac{1}{239}\right) = \pi/4,$$
$$6\tan^{-1}\left(\tfrac{1}{8}\right) + 2\tan^{-1}\left(\tfrac{1}{57}\right) + \tan^{-1}\left(\tfrac{1}{239}\right) = \pi/4.$$

The first of these formulas is called Machin's Formula. John Machin (1680–1751) used the formula to calculate the first 100 decimal places of π.

Such formulas were used to calculate π to a million decimal places in 1974.

More recently, highly ingenious methods (based on techniques due to Gauss for evaluating integrals approximately) have been used to calculate π correct to many billions of decimal places.

For your interest, we now list the first 1000 decimal places of π.

3.1415926535 8979323846 2643383279 5028841971 6939937510 5820974944 5923078164 0628620899 8628034825 3421170679
8214808651 3282306647 0938446095 5058223172 5359408128 4811174502 8410270193 8521105559 6446229489 5493038196
4428810975 6659334461 2847564823 3786783165 2712019091 4564856692 3460348610 4543266482 1339360726 0249141273
7245870066 0631558817 4881520920 9628292540 9171536436 7892590360 0113305305 4882046652 1384146951 9415116094
3305727036 5759591953 0921861173 8193261179 3105118548 0744623799 6274956735 1885752724 8912279381 8301194912
9833673362 4406566430 8602139494 6395224737 1907021798 6094370277 0539217176 2931767523 8467481846 7669405132
0005681271 4526356082 7785771342 7577896091 7363717872 1468440901 2249534301 4654958537 1050792279 6892589235
4201995611 2129021960 8640344181 5981362977 4771309960 5187072113 4999999837 2978049951 0597317328 1609631859
5024459455 3469083026 4252230825 3344685035 2619311881 7101000313 7838752886 5875332083 8142061717 7669147303
5982534904 2875546873 1159562863 8823537875 9375195778 1857780532 1712268066 1300192787 6611195909 2164201989

Watch the video programme 'Calculating π'.

Video

5.2 Review of the video programme

We begin by reviewing early estimates for π, including the following.

Babylonians	*c.* 2000 BC	$\pi = 3\frac{1}{8} = 3.125$
Egyptians	*c.* 2000 BC	$\pi = \frac{256}{81} \simeq 3.160$
Old Testament	*c.* 550 BC	$\pi = 3$
Archimedes	*c.* 300–200 BC	$\pi \simeq 3.141$
Chinese	*c.* AD 400–500	$\pi \simeq 3.141\,5926$
Hindus	*c.* AD 500–600	$\pi \simeq \sqrt{10} \simeq 3.16$

Old Testament references are
  1 Kings 7 : 23,
  2 Chronicles 4 : 2.

With the development of calculus in the seventeenth century, new formulas for estimating π were discovered, including the following.

Wallis' Formula $\quad \dfrac{\pi}{2} = \dfrac{2}{1} \cdot \dfrac{2}{3} \cdot \dfrac{4}{3} \cdot \dfrac{4}{5} \cdot \dfrac{6}{5} \cdot \dfrac{6}{7} \cdots$

See Unit AB3, Section 3.

Leibniz's series $\quad \tan^{-1} x = x - \dfrac{x^3}{3} + \dfrac{x^5}{5} - \dfrac{x^7}{7} + \cdots$

Gregory's series $\quad \dfrac{\pi}{4} = 1 - \dfrac{1}{3} + \dfrac{1}{5} - \dfrac{1}{7} + \cdots$

Often, the names Leibniz's series and Gregory's series are interchanged.

In the programme we review the theoretical basis for the latter two series, namely Taylor's Theorem and the Integration Rule for power series, and we discuss the formulas for $\pi/4$ given in Subsection 5.1.

The programme also gives two mnemonics that can be used to recall the first few digits for π, one of which is:

The word lengths give the successive digits of π.

May I have a large container of coffee?
3. 1   4   1   5   9   2   6

5.3 Proof that π is irrational

Finally, we prove that π is irrational.

> **Theorem 5.1** The number π is irrational.

The first proof that π is irrational was given by J. H. Lambert in 1766. This elegant, shorter proof was found by I. Niven in 1947.

Proof   We prove that π^2 is irrational, from which it follows that π is irrational. The proof is by contradiction and the method is rather unusual, so we begin by outlining the two major steps.

If you are short of time, omit this proof.

First we show that if f is any polynomial function such that

$$0 < f''(x) + \pi^2 f(x) < 1, \quad \text{for } 0 < x < 1, \tag{5.1}$$

then

$$0 < f(0) + f(1) < \frac{1}{\pi}. \tag{5.2}$$

Next we show that if $\pi^2 = a/b$, for $a, b \in \mathbb{N}$, then there is a polynomial function f such that statement (5.1) is true but statement (5.2) is false. This contradiction shows that π^2 must be irrational.

Let f be a polynomial function satisfying statement (5.1), and put

$$g(x) = f'(x) \sin \pi x - \pi f(x) \cos \pi x.$$

Then

$$g'(x) = f''(x) \sin \pi x + f'(x) \pi \cos \pi x - \pi f'(x) \cos \pi x + \pi^2 f(x) \sin \pi x$$
$$= \left(f''(x) + \pi^2 f(x) \right) \sin \pi x.$$

By the Mean Value Theorem, there exists $c \in (0,1)$ such that

See Unit AB2, Section 4.

$$g(1) - g(0) = g'(c) = \left(f''(c) + \pi^2 f(c) \right) \sin \pi c.$$

Hence $0 < g(1) - g(0) < 1$, by statement (5.1) and the fact that $0 < \sin \pi c \leq 1$. But

$$g(1) - g(0) = \pi(f(0) + f(1)),$$

by the definition of g, so statement (5.2) follows.

Now suppose that $\pi^2 = a/b$, where $a, b \in \mathbb{N}$. Take $N \in \mathbb{N}$ so large that $\pi^2 a^N / N! < 1$, and put

Recall that $\{a^n/n!\}$ is a basic null sequence; see Unit AA2, Section 2.

$$p(x) = \frac{1}{N!} x^N (1-x)^N \tag{5.3}$$
$$= \frac{1}{N!} \left(c_N x^N + c_{N+1} x^{N+1} + \cdots + c_{2N} x^{2N} \right),$$

where the coefficients c_k are integers, for $N \leq k \leq 2N$. Then we have

$$0 < p(x) < 1/N!, \quad \text{for } 0 < x < 1, \tag{5.4}$$

by equation (5.3). Also, for $k = 0, 1, \ldots,$

$$p^{(k)}(0) = \begin{cases} 0, & 0 \leq k < N, \ k > 2N, \\ c_k k!/N!, & N \leq k \leq 2N, \end{cases}$$

so $p^{(k)}(0)$ is an integer. Hence $p^{(k)}(1)$ is also an integer, by the symmetry of the function p under the change of variable $x' = 1 - x$.

Now consider the polynomial function

$$f(x) = a^N p(x) - a^{N-1} b\, p^{(2)}(x) + \cdots + (-1)^N b^N p^{(2N)}(x),$$

which has degree $2N$. Then $f(0)$ and $f(1)$ are both integers, so statement (5.2) is false. Finally,

$$f''(x) = a^N p^{(2)}(x) - a^{N-1} b\, p^{(4)}(x) + \cdots + (-1)^{N-1} a b^{N-1} p^{(2N)}(x),$$

since $p^{(2N+2)} = 0$. Hence

$$f''(x) + \pi^2 f(x) = f''(x) + \frac{a}{b} f(x) = \pi^2 a^N p(x),$$

by telescoping cancellation. Thus, by statement (5.4) and our choice of N,

$$0 < f''(x) + \pi^2 f(x) < \pi^2 a^N / N! < 1, \quad \text{for } 0 < x < 1,$$

so statement (5.1) does hold. This completes the proof. ∎

Solutions to the exercises

1.1 The tangent approximation to f at a is
$$f(x) \simeq f(a) + f'(a)(x - a).$$
(a) We have
$$f(x) = e^x, \quad f(2) = e^2;$$
$$f'(x) = e^x, \quad f'(2) = e^2.$$
Hence the tangent approximation to f at 2 is
$$e^x \simeq e^2 + e^2(x - 2).$$
(b) We have
$$f(x) = \cos x, \quad f(0) = 1;$$
$$f'(x) = -\sin x, \quad f'(0) = 0.$$
Hence the tangent approximation to f at 0 is
$$\cos x \simeq 1 + 0(x - 0) = 1.$$

1.2 (a) We have
$$f(x) = e^x, \quad f(2) = e^2;$$
$$f'(x) = e^x, \quad f'(2) = e^2;$$
$$f''(x) = e^x, \quad f''(2) = e^2;$$
$$f^{(3)}(x) = e^x, \quad f^{(3)}(2) = e^2.$$
Hence
$$T_1(x) = f(2) + f'(2)(x - 2) = e^2 + e^2(x - 2);$$
$$T_2(x) = f(2) + f'(2)(x - 2) + \frac{f''(2)}{2!}(x - 2)^2$$
$$= e^2 + e^2(x - 2) + \tfrac{1}{2}e^2(x - 2)^2;$$
$$T_3(x) = f(2) + f'(2)(x - 2) + \frac{f''(2)}{2!}(x - 2)^2$$
$$+ \frac{f^{(3)}(2)}{3!}(x - 2)^3$$
$$= e^2 + e^2(x - 2) + \tfrac{1}{2}e^2(x - 2)^2 + \tfrac{1}{6}e^2(x - 2)^3.$$
(b) We have
$$f(x) = \cos x, \quad f(0) = 1;$$
$$f'(x) = -\sin x, \quad f'(0) = 0;$$
$$f''(x) = -\cos x, \quad f''(0) = -1;$$
$$f^{(3)}(x) = \sin x, \quad f^{(3)}(0) = 0.$$
Hence
$$T_1(x) = f(0) + f'(0)x = 1;$$
$$T_2(x) = f(0) + f'(0)x + \frac{f''(0)}{2!}x^2 = 1 - \tfrac{1}{2}x^2;$$
$$T_3(x) = f(0) + f'(0)x + \frac{f''(0)}{2!}x^2 + \frac{f^{(3)}(0)}{3!}x^3$$
$$= 1 - \tfrac{1}{2}x^2.$$

1.3 The Taylor polynomial of degree 4 for f at a is
$$T_4(x) = f(a) + f'(a)(x - a) + \frac{f''(a)}{2!}(x - a)^2$$
$$+ \frac{f^{(3)}(a)}{3!}(x - a)^3 + \frac{f^{(4)}(a)}{4!}(x - a)^4.$$
(a) We have
$$f(x) = \log_e(1 + x), \quad f(0) = 0;$$
$$f'(x) = 1/(1 + x), \quad f'(0) = 1;$$
$$f''(x) = -1/(1 + x)^2, \quad f''(0) = -1;$$
$$f^{(3)}(x) = 2/(1 + x)^3, \quad f^{(3)}(0) = 2;$$
$$f^{(4)}(x) = -3!/(1 + x)^4, \quad f^{(4)}(0) = -3!.$$
Hence
$$T_4(x) = x - \tfrac{1}{2}x^2 + \tfrac{1}{3}x^3 - \tfrac{1}{4}x^4.$$
(b) We have
$$f(x) = \sin x, \quad f(\pi/4) = 1/\sqrt{2};$$
$$f'(x) = \cos x, \quad f'(\pi/4) = 1/\sqrt{2};$$
$$f''(x) = -\sin x, \quad f''(\pi/4) = -1/\sqrt{2};$$
$$f^{(3)}(x) = -\cos x, \quad f^{(3)}(\pi/4) = -1/\sqrt{2};$$
$$f^{(4)}(x) = \sin x, \quad f^{(4)}(\pi/4) = 1/\sqrt{2}.$$
Hence
$$T_4(x) = \frac{1}{\sqrt{2}}\left(1 + \left(x - \frac{\pi}{4}\right) - \frac{1}{2}\left(x - \frac{\pi}{4}\right)^2 \right.$$
$$\left. - \frac{1}{6}\left(x - \frac{\pi}{4}\right)^3 + \frac{1}{24}\left(x - \frac{\pi}{4}\right)^4\right).$$
(c) We have
$$f(x) = 1 + \tfrac{1}{2}x - \tfrac{1}{2}x^2 - \tfrac{1}{6}x^3 + \tfrac{1}{4}x^4, \quad f(0) = 1;$$
$$f'(x) = \tfrac{1}{2} - x - \tfrac{1}{2}x^2 + x^3, \quad f'(0) = \tfrac{1}{2};$$
$$f''(x) = -1 - x + 3x^2, \quad f''(0) = -1;$$
$$f^{(3)}(x) = -1 + 6x, \quad f^{(3)}(0) = -1;$$
$$f^{(4)}(x) = 6, \quad f^{(4)}(0) = 6.$$
Hence
$$T_4(x) = 1 + \tfrac{1}{2}x - \tfrac{1}{2}x^2 - \tfrac{1}{6}x^3 + \tfrac{1}{4}x^4.$$

1.4 From Example 1.2(a), we have
$$T_3(x) = x - \tfrac{1}{6}x^3,$$
so
$$T_3(0.1) = 0.1 - 0.001/6 = 0.099\,8\overline{3}.$$
Since
$$\sin(0.1) = 0.099\,833\,416\ldots,$$
we have
$$|\sin(0.1) - T_3(0.1)| = 0.099\,833\,416\ldots - 0.099\,8\overline{3}$$
$$\leq 0.099\,833\,417 - 0.099\,833\,333$$
$$= 0.000\,000\,084 < 1 \times 10^{-7},$$
as required.

1.5 (a) We have
$$f(x) = \log_e(1+x), \qquad f(0) = 0;$$
$$f'(x) = 1/(1+x), \qquad f'(0) = 1;$$
$$f''(x) = -1/(1+x)^2, \quad f''(0) = -1;$$
$$f^{(3)}(x) = 2/(1+x)^3, \quad f^{(3)}(0) = 2;$$
$$\vdots \qquad\qquad \vdots$$
$$f^{(n)}(x) = \frac{(-1)^{n+1}(n-1)!}{(1+x)^n}, \ f^{(n)}(0) = (-1)^{n+1}(n-1)!.$$
Hence
$$T_n(x) = x - \tfrac{1}{2}x^2 + \tfrac{1}{3}x^3 - \cdots + (-1)^{n+1}\frac{x^n}{n}.$$

(b) We have
$$f(x) = e^x, \quad f(0) = 1;$$
in general, for each positive integer k,
$$f^{(k)}(x) = e^x, \quad f^{(k)}(0) = 1.$$
Hence
$$T_n(x) = 1 + x + \frac{x^2}{2!} + \cdots + \frac{x^n}{n!}.$$

(c) We have
$$f(x) = \sin x, \qquad f(0) = 0;$$
$$f'(x) = \cos x, \qquad f'(0) = 1;$$
$$f''(x) = -\sin x, \qquad f''(0) = 0;$$
$$f^{(3)}(x) = -\cos x, \quad f^{(3)}(0) = -1;$$
$$f^{(4)}(x) = \sin x, \qquad f^{(4)}(0) = 0;$$
in general, for $k = 0, 1, 2, \ldots,$
$$f^{(2k)}(0) = 0 \quad \text{and} \quad f^{(2k+1)}(0) = (-1)^k.$$
Hence, for $k = 0, 1, 2, \ldots,$
$$T_{2k+1}(x) = x - \frac{x^3}{3!} + \frac{x^5}{5!} + \cdots + (-1)^k\frac{x^{2k+1}}{(2k+1)!}$$
and $T_{2k+2}(x) = T_{2k+1}(x)$.

(d) We have
$$f(x) = \cos x, \qquad f(0) = 1;$$
$$f'(x) = -\sin x, \qquad f'(0) = 0;$$
$$f''(x) = -\cos x, \qquad f''(0) = -1;$$
$$f^{(3)}(x) = \sin x, \qquad f^{(3)}(0) = 0;$$
$$f^{(4)}(x) = \cos x, \qquad f^{(4)}(0) = 1;$$
in general, for $k = 0, 1, 2, \ldots,$
$$f^{(2k)}(0) = (-1)^k \quad \text{and} \quad f^{(2k+1)}(0) = 0.$$
Hence, for $k = 0, 1, 2, \ldots,$
$$T_{2k}(x) = 1 - \frac{x^2}{2!} + \frac{x^4}{4!} + \cdots + (-1)^k\frac{x^{2k}}{(2k)!}$$
and $T_{2k+1}(x) = T_{2k}(x)$.

1.6 (a) We have
$$f(x) = 2 - 3x + x^2 + e^x, \quad f(0) = 3;$$
$$f'(x) = -3 + 2x + e^x, \qquad f'(0) = -2.$$
Hence the tangent approximation at 0 to f is
$$f(x) \simeq 3 - 2(x - 0) = 3 - 2x.$$

(b) We have
$$f(x) = 2 - 3x + x^2 + e^x, \quad f(1) = e;$$
$$f'(x) = -3 + 2x + e^x, \qquad f'(1) = -1 + e.$$
Hence the tangent approximation at 1 to f is
$$f(x) \simeq e + (e-1)(x-1).$$

1.7 (a) We have
$$f(x) = \log_e(1+x) \qquad f(2) = \log_e 3;$$
$$f'(x) = 1/(1+x), \qquad f'(2) = 1/3;$$
$$f''(x) = -1/(1+x)^2 \quad f''(2) = -1/9;$$
$$f^{(3)}(x) = 2/(1+x)^3, \quad f^{(3)}(2) = 2/27.$$
Hence
$$T_3(x) = \log_e 3 + \tfrac{1}{3}(x-2) - \tfrac{1}{18}(x-2)^2 + \tfrac{1}{81}(x-2)^3.$$

(b) We have
$$f(x) = \sin x, \qquad f(\pi/6) = 1/2;$$
$$f'(x) = \cos x, \qquad f'(\pi/6) = \sqrt{3}/2;$$
$$f''(x) = -\sin x, \qquad f''(\pi/6) = -1/2;$$
$$f^{(3)}(x) = -\cos x, \quad f^{(3)}(\pi/6) = -\sqrt{3}/2.$$
Hence
$$T_3(x) = \frac{1}{2} + \frac{\sqrt{3}}{2}\left(x - \frac{\pi}{6}\right) - \frac{1}{4}\left(x - \frac{\pi}{6}\right)^2$$
$$- \frac{\sqrt{3}}{12}\left(x - \frac{\pi}{6}\right)^3.$$

(c) We have
$$f(x) = (1+x)^{-2}, \qquad f(\tfrac{1}{2}) = 4/9;$$
$$f'(x) = -2(1+x)^{-3}, \qquad f'(\tfrac{1}{2}) = -16/27;$$
$$f''(x) = 6(1+x)^{-4}, \qquad f''(\tfrac{1}{2}) = 32/27;$$
$$f^{(3)}(x) = -24(1+x)^{-5}, \quad f^{(3)}(\tfrac{1}{2}) = -256/81.$$
Hence
$$T_3(x) = \tfrac{4}{9} - \tfrac{16}{27}(x - \tfrac{1}{2}) + \tfrac{16}{27}(x - \tfrac{1}{2})^2 - \tfrac{128}{243}(x - \tfrac{1}{2})^3.$$

(d) We have
$$f(x) = \tan x, \qquad\qquad f(\pi/4) = 1;$$
$$f'(x) = \sec^2 x, \qquad\qquad f'(\pi/4) = 2;$$
$$f''(x) = 2\sec^2 x \tan x, \qquad\qquad f''(\pi/4) = 4;$$
$$f^{(3)}(x) = 4\sec^2 x \tan^2 x + 2\sec^4 x, \quad f^{(3)}(\pi/4) = 16.$$
Hence
$$T_3(x) = 1 + 2\left(x - \frac{\pi}{4}\right) + 2\left(x - \frac{\pi}{4}\right)^2 + \frac{8}{3}\left(x - \frac{\pi}{4}\right)^3.$$

1.8 (a) We have
$$f(x) = \cosh x, \qquad f(0) = 1;$$
$$f'(x) = \sinh x, \qquad f'(0) = 0;$$
$$f''(x) = \cosh x, \qquad f''(0) = 1;$$
$$f^{(3)}(x) = \sinh x, \quad f^{(3)}(0) = 0;$$
$$f^{(4)}(x) = \cosh x, \quad f^{(4)}(0) = 1.$$
Hence
$$T_4(x) = 1 + \tfrac{1}{2}x^2 + \tfrac{1}{24}x^4.$$

(b) We have

$$f(x) = x^5, \qquad f(1) = 1;$$
$$f'(x) = 5x^4, \qquad f'(1) = 5;$$
$$f''(x) = 20x^3, \qquad f''(1) = 20;$$
$$f^{(3)}(x) = 60x^2, \quad f^{(3)}(1) = 60;$$
$$f^{(4)}(x) = 120x, \quad f^{(4)}(1) = 120.$$

Hence

$$T_4(x) = 1 + 5(x-1) + 10(x-1)^2 + 10(x-1)^3$$
$$+ 5(x-1)^4.$$

1.9 From Exercise 1.5(b), we have

$$T_3(x) = 1 + x + \frac{x^2}{2!} + \frac{x^3}{3!},$$

so

$$T_3(0.1) = 1 + 0.1 + \tfrac{1}{2}(0.1)^2 + \tfrac{1}{6}(0.1)^3$$
$$= 1.105\,1\overline{6}.$$

Since

$$e^{0.1} = 1.105\,170\,918\ldots,$$

we have

$$|e^{0.1} - T_3(0.1)| = 1.105\,170\,918\ldots - 1.105\,1\overline{6}$$
$$\leq 1.105\,170\,919 - 1.105\,166\,666$$
$$= 0.000\,004\,253\ldots < 5 \times 10^{-6},$$

as required.

2.1 We have

$$f(x) = \cos x, \qquad f(0) = 1;$$
$$f'(x) = -\sin x, \qquad f'(0) = 0;$$
$$f''(x) = -\cos x, \qquad f''(0) = -1;$$
$$f^{(3)}(x) = \sin x, \qquad f^{(3)}(0) = 0;$$
$$f^{(4)}(x) = \cos x.$$

Hence, by Taylor's Theorem with $a = 0$, $f(x) = \cos x$ and $n = 3$,

$$\cos x = 1 - \tfrac{1}{2}x^2 + R_3(x),$$

where

$$R_3(x) = \frac{f^{(4)}(c)}{4!}\, x^4 = \frac{\cos c}{4!}\, x^4,$$

for some c between 0 and x, as required.

2.2 (a) By the solution to Exercise 1.5(a), we have

$$T_2(x) = x - \tfrac{1}{2}x^2.$$

(b) We use Strategy 2.1 with $a = 0$, $x = 0.02$ and $n = 2$.

1. First, $f^{(3)}(x) = \dfrac{2}{(1+x)^3}$; see Exercise 1.5(a).

2. Thus
$$|f^{(3)}(c)| = \frac{2}{(1+c)^3} \leq 2, \quad \text{for } c \in [0, 0.2],$$
so we can take $M = 2$.

3. Hence
$$|\log_e(1.02) - T_2(0.02)| = |R_2(0.02)|$$
$$\leq \frac{M}{(2+1)!}|x-a|^{2+1}$$
$$= \frac{2}{3!} \times |0.02 - 0|^3$$
$$= 0.000\,002\overline{6}$$
$$< 3 \times 10^{-6},$$
as required.

(c) By part (a),
$$T_2(0.02) = 0.02 - \tfrac{1}{2}(0.02)^2 = 0.0198.$$
By part (b),
$$|\log_e(1.02) - T_2(0.02)| < 0.000\,003.$$
Hence
$$0.019\,797 < \log_e(1.02) < 0.019\,803,$$
so
$$\log_e(1.02) = 0.0198 \text{ (to 4 d.p.)}.$$

2.3 (a) Using the formulas in the solution to Exercise 1.5(d), we obtain

$$f(\pi) = -1, \quad f'(\pi) = 0, \quad f''(\pi) = 1,$$
$$f^{(3)}(\pi) = 0, \quad f^{(4)}(\pi) = -1.$$

Hence

$$T_4(x) = -1 + \tfrac{1}{2}(x-\pi)^2 - \tfrac{1}{24}(x-\pi)^4.$$

(b) We use Strategy 2.2 with $I = \left[\tfrac{3}{4}\pi, \tfrac{5}{4}\pi\right]$, $a = \pi$, $r = \tfrac{1}{4}\pi$ and $n = 4$.

1. First, $f^{(5)}(x) = -\sin x$; see Exercise 1.5(d).

2. Thus
$$|f^{(5)}(c)| \leq 1, \quad \text{for } c \in \left[\tfrac{3}{4}\pi, \tfrac{5}{4}\pi\right],$$
so we can take $M = 1$.

3. Hence
$$|R_4(x)| \leq \frac{M}{(4+1)!}\, r^{4+1}$$
$$= \frac{1}{5!}\left(\tfrac{1}{4}\pi\right)^5$$
$$= 0.002\,49\ldots$$
$$< 3 \times 10^{-3}, \quad \text{for } x \in \left[\tfrac{3}{4}\pi, \tfrac{5}{4}\pi\right].$$

Thus $T_4(x)$ approximates $f(x)$ with an error less than 3×10^{-3} on $\left[\tfrac{3}{4}\pi, \tfrac{5}{4}\pi\right]$.

2.4 We have

$$f(x) = \sin x, \qquad f(\pi/4) = 1/\sqrt{2};$$
$$f'(x) = \cos x, \qquad f'(\pi/4) = 1/\sqrt{2};$$
$$f''(x) = -\sin x, \qquad f''(\pi/4) = -1/\sqrt{2};$$
$$f^{(3)}(x) = -\cos x.$$

Hence, by applying Taylor's Theorem to f at $a = \pi/4$, with $n = 2$, we obtain

$$\sin x = \frac{1}{\sqrt{2}} + \frac{1}{\sqrt{2}}\left(x - \frac{\pi}{4}\right) - \frac{1}{2\sqrt{2}}\left(x - \frac{\pi}{4}\right)^2 + R_2(x),$$

where

$$R_2(x) = \frac{f^{(3)}(c)}{3!}\left(x - \frac{\pi}{4}\right)^3 = -\frac{\cos c}{6}\left(x - \frac{\pi}{4}\right)^3,$$

for some c between 0 and x, as required.

2.5 We have

$$\begin{aligned}
f(x) &= \sinh x, & f(0) &= 0;\\
f'(x) &= \cosh x, & f'(0) &= 1;\\
f''(x) &= \sinh x, & f''(0) &= 0;\\
f^{(3)}(x) &= \cosh x, & f^{(3)}(0) &= 1;\\
f^{(4)}(x) &= \sinh x, & f^{(4)}(0) &= 0.
\end{aligned}$$

Hence, with $a = 0$,

$$T_4(x) = x + \frac{1}{3!}x^3 = x + \frac{1}{6}x^3.$$

Now we use Strategy 2.1 with $a = 0$, $x = 0.2$ and $n = 4$. First,

$$f^{(5)}(x) = \cosh x,$$

so, for $c \in [0, 0.2]$, we have

$$|f^{(5)}(c)| = \cosh c \leq \cosh(0.2) \leq \cosh 1.$$

Now

$$\cosh 1 = \tfrac{1}{2}(e + e^{-1}) < \tfrac{1}{2}(3 + 1/2) = 7/4,$$

so we can take $M = 7/4$. Thus

$$\begin{aligned}
|f(0.2) - T_4(0.2)| &= |R_4(0.2)|\\
&\leq \frac{M}{(4+1)!}|x - a|^{4+1}\\
&= \frac{7/4}{5!}|0.2 - 0|^5\\
&= 4.\overline{6} \times 10^{-6} < 5 \times 10^{-6}.
\end{aligned}$$

Finally,

$$T_4(0.2) = 0.2 + \tfrac{1}{6}(0.2)^3 = 0.201\overline{3},$$

so

$$\sinh(0.2) = 0.2013 \text{ (to 4 d.p.)}.$$

2.6 **(a)** We have

$$\begin{aligned}
f(x) &= x/(x + 3), & f(2) &= 2/5;\\
f'(x) &= 3/(x+3)^2, & f'(2) &= 3/25;\\
f''(x) &= -6/(x+3)^3, & f''(2) &= -6/125;\\
f^{(3)}(x) &= 18/(x+3)^4, & f^{(3)}(2) &= 18/625.
\end{aligned}$$

Hence

$$T_3(x) = \tfrac{2}{5} + \tfrac{3}{25}(x - 2) - \tfrac{3}{125}(x - 2)^2 + \tfrac{3}{625}(x - 2)^3.$$

(b) We use Strategy 2.2 with $I = \left[2, \frac{5}{2}\right]$, $a = 2$, $r = \frac{1}{2}$ and $n = 3$.

1. First, $f^{(4)}(x) = -72/(x + 3)^5$.

2. Thus

$$|f^{(4)}(c)| = \frac{72}{(c+3)^5} \leq \frac{72}{5^5}, \quad \text{for } c \in \left[2, \tfrac{5}{2}\right],$$

so we can take $M = 72/5^5$.

3. Hence

$$\begin{aligned}
|R_3(x)| &\leq \frac{M}{(3+1)!}r^{3+1}\\
&= \frac{1}{4!} \times \frac{72}{5^5}\left(\frac{1}{2}\right)^4\\
&= \frac{3}{5^5}\left(\frac{1}{2}\right)^4 = 6 \times 10^{-5}.
\end{aligned}$$

Thus $T_3(x)$ approximates $f(x)$ to within 6×10^{-5} on $\left[2, \frac{5}{2}\right]$.

3.1 **(a)** Here $a_n = 2^n + 4^n$, for $n = 0, 1, 2, \ldots$, so

$$\begin{aligned}
\left|\frac{a_{n+1}}{a_n}\right| &= \frac{2^{n+1} + 4^{n+1}}{2^n + 4^n}\\
&= \frac{2(1/2)^n + 4}{(1/2)^n + 1} \to 4 \text{ as } n \to \infty.
\end{aligned}$$

Hence, by the Ratio Test, the radius of convergence is $R = \frac{1}{4}$.

(b) Here $a_n = (n!)^2/(2n)!$, for $n = 1, 2, \ldots$, so

$$\begin{aligned}
\left|\frac{a_{n+1}}{a_n}\right| &= \frac{((n+1)!)^2}{(2n+2)!} \times \frac{(2n)!}{(n!)^2}\\
&= \frac{(n+1)(n+1)}{(2n+2)(2n+1)}\\
&= \frac{(1+1/n)(1+1/n)}{(2+2/n)(2+1/n)} \to \frac{1}{4} \text{ as } n \to \infty.
\end{aligned}$$

Hence, by the Ratio Test, the radius of convergence is $R = 4$.

(c) Here $a_n = n + 2^{-n}$, for $n = 0, 1, 2, \ldots$, so

$$\begin{aligned}
\left|\frac{a_{n+1}}{a_n}\right| &= \frac{n + 1 + 2^{-n-1}}{n + 2^{-n}}\\
&= \frac{1 + 1/n + 1/(n2^{n+1})}{1 + 1/(n2^n)} \to 1 \text{ as } n \to \infty.
\end{aligned}$$

Hence, by the Ratio Test, the radius of convergence is $R = 1$.

(d) Here $a_n = n^n$, for $n = 1, 2, \ldots$, so

$$\begin{aligned}
\left|\frac{a_{n+1}}{a_n}\right| &= \frac{(n+1)^{(n+1)}}{n^n}\\
&= (n+1)\left(\frac{n+1}{n}\right)^n \to \infty \text{ as } n \to \infty.
\end{aligned}$$

Hence, by the Ratio Test, the radius of convergence is $R = 0$; that is, the series converges only for $x = 0$.

3.2 Applying the Ratio Test with
$$a_n = \frac{\alpha(\alpha-1)\cdots(\alpha-n+1)}{n!},$$
we obtain, for $\alpha \neq 0, 1, \ldots,$
$$\left|\frac{a_{n+1}}{a_n}\right|$$
$$= \left|\frac{\alpha(\alpha-1)\cdots(\alpha-n)}{(n+1)!} \times \frac{n!}{\alpha(\alpha-1)\cdots(\alpha-n+1)}\right|$$
$$= \left|\frac{\alpha-n}{n+1}\right|$$
$$= \left|\frac{(\alpha/n)-1}{1+1/n}\right| \to 1 \text{ as } n \to \infty.$$
Hence the radius of convergence is 1.

3.3 In each case, we apply Strategy 3.1.

(a) Here $a_n = n$, for $n = 1, 2, \ldots.$

1. Since
$$\left|\frac{a_{n+1}}{a_n}\right| = \frac{n+1}{n}$$
$$= 1 + 1/n \to 1 \text{ as } n \to \infty,$$
we have $R = 1$, by the Ratio Test. Thus this power series

converges for $-1 < x < 1$,

diverges for $x > 1$ and $x < -1$.

2. If $x = 1$, then the power series is
$$\sum_{n=0}^{\infty} n(1)^n = \sum_{n=0}^{\infty} n, \text{ which is divergent,}$$
by the Non-null Test.

If $x = -1$, then the power series is
$$\sum_{n=0}^{\infty} n(-1)^n = \sum_{n=0}^{\infty} (-1)^n n, \text{ which is divergent,}$$
by the Non-null Test.

Hence the interval of convergence is $(-1, 1)$.

(b) Here $a_n = (-1)^n/(n3^n)$, for $n = 1, 2, \ldots.$

1. Since
$$\left|\frac{a_{n+1}}{a_n}\right| = \frac{1}{(n+1)3^{n+1}} \times \frac{n3^n}{1}$$
$$= \frac{1}{(1+1/n)3} \to \frac{1}{3} \text{ as } n \to \infty,$$
we have $R = 3$, by the Ratio Test. Since $a = 5$, this power series

converges for $2 < x < 8$,

diverges for $x > 8$ and $x < 2$.

2. If $x = 8$, then the power series is
$$\sum_{n=1}^{\infty} \frac{(-1)^n}{n3^n}(8-5)^n = \sum_{n=1}^{\infty} \frac{(-1)^n}{n},$$
which is convergent, by the Alternating Test.

If $x = 2$, then the power series is
$$\sum_{n=1}^{\infty} \frac{(-1)^n}{n3^n}(2-5)^n = \sum_{n=1}^{\infty} \frac{1}{n},$$
which is a basic divergent series.

Hence the interval of convergence is $(2, 8]$.

3.4 (a) Here $a_n = (3n)!/(n!)^2$, for $n = 0, 1, 2, \ldots,$ so
$$\left|\frac{a_{n+1}}{a_n}\right| = \frac{(3n+3)!}{((n+1)!)^2} \times \frac{(n!)^2}{(3n)!}$$
$$= \frac{(3n+3)(3n+2)(3n+1)}{(n+1)(n+1)}$$
$$= \frac{(3+3/n)(3+2/n)}{(1+1/n)(1+1/n)}(3n+1)$$
$$\to \infty \text{ as } n \to \infty.$$
Hence, by the Ratio Test, the radius of convergence is 0; the power series converges only when $x = -2$.

(b) Here $a_n = n!/n^n$, for $n = 1, 2, \ldots,$ so
$$\left|\frac{a_{n+1}}{a_n}\right| = \frac{(n+1)!}{(n+1)^{n+1}} \times \frac{n^n}{n!}$$
$$= \left(\frac{n}{n+1}\right)^n$$
$$= 1/(1+1/n)^n \to 1/e \text{ as } n \to \infty.$$
Hence, by the Ratio Test, the radius of convergence is e.

(c) Here $a_n = 1/(n+1)^n$, for $n = 0, 1, 2, \ldots,$ so
$$\left|\frac{a_{n+1}}{a_n}\right| = \frac{1}{(n+2)^{n+1}} \times \frac{(n+1)^n}{1}$$
$$= \frac{(n+1)^n}{(n+2)^n} \times \frac{1}{n+2}$$
$$\leq \frac{1}{n+2} \to 0 \text{ as } n \to \infty.$$
Hence, by the Ratio Test, the power series converges for all x; that is, $R = \infty$.

3.5 In each case, we apply Strategy 3.1.

(a) Here $a_n = 2^n/n!$, for $n = 0, 1, 2, \ldots.$

1. Since
$$\left|\frac{a_{n+1}}{a_n}\right| = \frac{2^{n+1}}{(n+1)!} \times \frac{n!}{2^n}$$
$$= \frac{2}{n+1} \to 0 \text{ as } n \to \infty,$$
we have $R = \infty$, by the Ratio Test.

Thus this power series converges for all x, so the interval of convergence is $\mathbb{R}$.

(In this case, there are no endpoints to check.)

(b) Here $a_n = 2^n/n$, for $n = 1, 2, \ldots$.

1. Since
$$\left| \frac{a_{n+1}}{a_n} \right| = \frac{2^{n+1}}{n+1} \times \frac{n}{2^n}$$
$$= \frac{2}{1 + 1/n} \to 2 \quad \text{as } n \to \infty,$$

we have $R = \frac{1}{2}$, by the Ratio Test. Since $a = -1$, this power series

    converges for $-\frac{3}{2} < x < -\frac{1}{2}$,

    diverges for $x > -\frac{1}{2}$ and $x < -\frac{3}{2}$.

2. If $x = -\frac{1}{2}$, then the power series is
$$\sum_{n=1}^{\infty} \frac{2^n}{n}(-\tfrac{1}{2} + 1)^n = \sum_{n=1}^{\infty} \frac{1}{n},$$

which is a basic divergent series.

If $x = -\frac{3}{2}$, then the power series is
$$\sum_{n=1}^{\infty} \frac{2^n}{n}(-\tfrac{3}{2} + 1)^n = \sum_{n=1}^{\infty} \frac{(-1)^n}{n},$$

which is convergent, by the Alternating Test.

Hence the interval of convergence is $[-\frac{3}{2}, -\frac{1}{2})$.

4.1 (a) We know that, for $x \in \mathbb{R}$,
$$e^x = 1 + x + \frac{x^2}{2!} + \frac{x^3}{3!} + \cdots + \frac{x^n}{n!} + \cdots$$
and
$$e^{-x} = 1 - x + \frac{x^2}{2!} - \frac{x^3}{3!} + \cdots + (-1)^n \frac{x^n}{n!} + \cdots.$$
Hence, by the Sum and Multiple Rules,
$$\sinh x = \tfrac{1}{2}(e^x - e^{-x})$$
$$= x + \frac{x^3}{3!} + \cdots + \frac{x^{2n+1}}{(2n+1)!} + \cdots,$$
for $x \in \mathbb{R}$.

(b) We know that, for $|x| < 1$,
$$\log_e(1 - x) = -x - \frac{x^2}{2} - \frac{x^3}{3} - \cdots - \frac{x^n}{n} - \cdots$$
and
$$(1 - x)^{-1} = 1 + x + x^2 + x^3 + \cdots + x^n + \cdots.$$
Hence, by the Sum and Multiple Rules,
$$\log_e(1 - x) + 2(1 - x)^{-1}$$
$$= \left(-x - \frac{x^2}{2} - \frac{x^3}{3} - \cdots - \frac{x^n}{n} - \cdots \right)$$
$$+ (2 + 2x + 2x^2 + 2x^3 + \cdots + 2x^n + \cdots)$$
$$= 2 + x + \frac{3}{2}x^2 + \frac{5}{3}x^3 + \cdots + \left(2 - \frac{1}{n} \right) x^n + \cdots,$$
for $|x| < 1$.

4.2 (a) We know that, for $|x| < 1$,
$$\log_e(1 + x) = x - \frac{x^2}{2} + \frac{x^3}{3} - \cdots + (-1)^{n+1}\frac{x^n}{n} + \cdots.$$
Hence, by the Product Rule,
$$(1 + x)\log_e(1 + x)$$
$$= \left(x - \frac{x^2}{2} + \frac{x^3}{3} - \cdots + (-1)^{n+1}\frac{x^n}{n} + \cdots \right)$$
$$+ \left(x^2 - \frac{x^3}{2} + \cdots + (-1)^n \frac{x^n}{n-1} + \cdots \right)$$
$$= x + \frac{x^2}{2} - \frac{x^3}{6} + \cdots + (-1)^n\frac{x^n}{n(n-1)} + \cdots,$$
for $|x| < 1$.

(b) We know that, for $|x| < 1$,
$$\frac{1}{1 - x} = 1 + x + x^2 + \cdots + x^n + \cdots,$$
and, for $|x| < 1$, from the results in Frame 7, that
$$\frac{1 + x}{(1 - x)^2} = 1 + 3x + 5x^2 + \cdots + (2n + 1)x^n + \cdots.$$
Hence, by the Product Rule,
$$\frac{1 + x}{(1 - x)^3} = (1 + x + x^2 + \cdots + x^n + \cdots)$$
$$\times (1 + 3x + 5x^2 + \cdots + (2n + 1)x^n + \cdots)$$
$$= 1 + (3 + 1)x + (5 + 3 + 1)x^2 + \cdots$$
$$+ ((2n + 1) + (2n - 1) + \cdots + 1)x^n + \cdots$$
$$= 1 + 4x + 9x^2 + \cdots + (n + 1)^2 x^2 + \cdots,$$
for $|x| < 1$, since $1 + 3 + \cdots + (2n + 1)$ is an arithmetic sequence with sum $(n + 1)^2$.

4.3 (a) We know that, for $|x| < 1$,
$$(1 - x)^{-1} = 1 + x + x^2 + \cdots + x^n + \cdots.$$
Hence, by the Differentiation Rule,
$$(1 - x)^{-2} = 1 + 2x + 3x^2 + \cdots + nx^{n-1} + \cdots,$$
for $|x| < 1$.

(b) Differentiating again, we obtain
$$2(1 - x)^{-3} = 2 + 6x + \cdots + n(n - 1)x^{n-2} + \cdots,$$
for $|x| < 1$.

Hence, by the Multiple Rule,
$$(1 - x)^{-3} = 1 + 3x + \cdots + \frac{n(n - 1)}{2}x^{n-2} + \cdots,$$
for $|x| < 1$.

(c) We have
$$f'(x) = \frac{1}{1 - x^2} = 1 + x^2 + x^4 + \cdots + x^{2n} + \cdots,$$
for $|x| < 1$. Thus, by the Integration Rule, the Taylor series at 0 for f is
$$f(x) = c + x + \frac{x^3}{3} + \frac{x^5}{5} + \cdots + \frac{x^{2n+1}}{2n + 1} + \cdots,$$
for $|x| < 1$. Since $f(0) = 0$, it follows that $c = 0$. Hence
$$\tanh^{-1} x = x + \frac{x^3}{3} + \frac{x^5}{5} + \cdots + \frac{x^{2n+1}}{2n + 1} + \cdots,$$
for $|x| < 1$.

4.4 (a) We know that, for $x \in \mathbb{R}$,
$$\sinh x = x + \frac{x^3}{3!} + \frac{x^5}{5!} + \cdots + \frac{x^{2n+1}}{(2n+1)!} + \cdots$$
and
$$\sin x = x - \frac{x^3}{3!} + \frac{x^5}{5!} - \cdots + (-1)^n \frac{x^{2n+1}}{(2n+1)!} + \cdots.$$
Hence, by the Sum Rule, for $x \in \mathbb{R}$,
$$\sinh x + \sin x$$
$$= 2x + \frac{2x^5}{5!} + \frac{2x^9}{9!} + \cdots + \frac{2x^{4n+1}}{(4n+1)!} + \cdots.$$

(b) We know that
$$\frac{1}{1+x} = 1 - x + x^2 - \cdots + (-1)^n x^n + \cdots,$$
for $|x| < 1$. Replacing x by $2x^2$, we obtain
$$\frac{1}{1+2x^2} = 1 - 2x^2 + 4x^4 - \cdots + (-1)^n 2^n x^{2n} + \cdots.$$
This last series converges for $2x^2 < 1$; that is, for $|x| < 1/\sqrt{2}$.

4.5 We know that
$$e^x = 1 + x + \frac{x^2}{2!} + \cdots + \frac{x^n}{n!} + \cdots, \quad \text{for } x \in \mathbb{R}.$$
Also, for $|x| < 1$, from Exercise 4.3(a),
$$(1-x)^{-2} = 1 + 2x + 3x^2 + \cdots + (n+1)x^n + \cdots.$$
Hence, by the Product Rule,
$$e^x (1-x)^{-2}$$
$$= \left(1 + x + \tfrac{1}{2}x^2 + \cdots\right)\left(1 + 2x + 3x^2 + \cdots\right)$$
$$= 1 + (2+1)x + \left(3 + 2 + \tfrac{1}{2}\right) x^2 + \cdots$$
$$= 1 + 3x + \tfrac{11}{2}x^2 + \cdots, \quad \text{for } |x| < 1.$$

4.6 Since
$$e^x = 1 + x + \frac{x^2}{2!} + \cdots + \frac{x^n}{n!} + \cdots, \quad \text{for } x \in \mathbb{R},$$
we have
$$e^{-x^2} = 1 - x^2 + \frac{x^4}{2!} - \cdots + (-1)^n \frac{x^{2n}}{n!} + \cdots,$$
for $x \in \mathbb{R}$. It follows from the Integration Rule that
$$\int_0^1 e^{-x^2}\, dx$$
$$= \left[x - \frac{x^3}{3} + \frac{x^5}{5 \times 2!} - \cdots + (-1)^n \frac{x^{2n+1}}{(2n+1)n!} + \cdots \right]_0^1$$
$$= 1 - \frac{1}{3} + \frac{1}{10} - \cdots + \frac{(-1)^n}{(2n+1)n!} + \cdots.$$

4.7 (a) The Taylor series at 0 for $1/(1+x)$ is
$$\frac{1}{1+x} = 1 - x + x^2 - \cdots = \sum_{n=0}^{\infty} (-1)^n x^n,$$
for $|x| < 1$.

(b) We know that
$$\frac{d}{dx} \log_e(1+x) = \frac{1}{1+x}.$$

By part (a), for $|x| < 1$,
$$\frac{1}{1+x} = 1 - x + x^2 - \cdots + (-1)^n x^n + \cdots.$$
Hence, by the Integration Rule,
$$\log_e(1+x) = c + x - \frac{x^2}{2} + \cdots + (-1)^n \frac{x^{n+1}}{n+1} + \cdots,$$
for $|x| < 1$, where c is a constant.
On substituting $x = 0$, we find that $c = 0$. Hence
$$\log_e(1+x) = x - \frac{x^2}{2} + \cdots + (-1)^{n+1}\frac{x^n}{n} + \cdots,$$
for $|x| < 1$. (Note that $(-1)^{n+1} = (-1)^{n-1}$.)

4.8 By the General Binomial Theorem (in Frame 13),
$$(1+x)^{-1/3} = \sum_{n=0}^{\infty} \binom{-\frac{1}{3}}{n} x^n, \quad \text{for } |x| < 1,$$
where
$$\binom{-\frac{1}{3}}{n} = \frac{(-\frac{1}{3})(-\frac{4}{3})(-\frac{7}{3}) \cdots (-\frac{1}{3} - n + 1)}{n!}.$$
Hence
$$(1+x)^{-1/3}$$
$$= 1 + \frac{(-\frac{1}{3})}{1} x + \frac{(-\frac{1}{3})(-\frac{4}{3})}{2!} x^2 + \cdots$$
$$= 1 - \tfrac{1}{3}x + \tfrac{2}{9}x^2 - \cdots, \quad \text{for } |x| < 1.$$

4.9 (a) We have
$$\log_e\left(\frac{1+2x}{1-2x}\right) = \log_e(1+2x) - \log_e(1-2x).$$
We know that, for $|x| < 1$,
$$\log_e(1+x) = x - \frac{x^2}{2} + \frac{x^3}{3} - \cdots + (-1)^{n+1}\frac{x^n}{n} + \cdots.$$
Thus, for $|2x| < 1$,
$$\log_e(1+2x)$$
$$= 2x - \frac{4x^2}{2} + \frac{8x^3}{3} - \cdots + (-1)^{n+1}\frac{2^n x^n}{n} + \cdots$$
and
$$\log_e(1-2x)$$
$$= -2x - \frac{4x^2}{2} - \frac{8x^3}{3} - \cdots - \frac{2^n x^n}{n} + \cdots.$$
Hence, by the Sum and Multiple Rules, for $|x| < 1/2$,
$$\log_e\left(\frac{1+2x}{1-2x}\right)$$
$$= \log_e(1+2x) - \log_e(1-2x)$$
$$= 4x + \frac{16x^3}{3} + \cdots + \frac{2^{2k+2}x^{2k+1}}{2k+1} + \cdots.$$

(b) We know that, for $|x| < 1$,
$$\frac{1}{1-x} = 1 + x + x^2 + \cdots + x^n + \cdots,$$
and we know from Frame 2 that, for $x \in \mathbb{R}$,
$$\cosh x = 1 + \frac{x^2}{2!} + \frac{x^4}{4!} + \cdots + \frac{x^{2n}}{(2n)!} + \cdots.$$

Hence, by the Product Rule,

$$\frac{\cosh x}{1-x}$$

$$= \left(1 + \frac{x^2}{2!} + \frac{x^4}{4!} + \cdots\right)\left(1 + x + x^2 + \cdots\right)$$

$$= 1 + x + \left(1 + \frac{1}{2!}\right)x^2 + \left(1 + \frac{1}{2!}\right)x^3$$

$$+ \left(1 + \frac{1}{2!} + \frac{1}{4!}\right)x^4 + \left(1 + \frac{1}{2!} + \frac{1}{4!}\right)x^5 + \cdots,$$

for $|x| < 1$. Thus, for $|x| < 1$,

$$\frac{\cosh x}{1-x} = \sum_{n=0}^{\infty} a_n x^n, \quad \text{where } a_n = \sum_{k=0}^{[n/2]} \frac{1}{(2k)!}.$$

4.10 By the Product Rule, for $x \in \mathbb{R}$,

$$f(x) = e^x \sin x$$

$$= \left(1 + x + \tfrac{1}{2}x^2 + \tfrac{1}{6}x^3 + \cdots\right)\left(x - \tfrac{1}{6}x^3 + \cdots\right)$$

$$= x - \tfrac{1}{6}x^3 + x^2 + \tfrac{1}{2}x^3$$

$$\quad + \text{ powers of } x \text{ greater than } 3$$

$$= x + x^2 + \tfrac{1}{3}x^3 + \cdots.$$

The series converges for all $x \in \mathbb{R}$ because the Taylor series for e^x and $\sin x$ both have radius of convergence ∞.

4.11 (a) By the General Binomial Theorem,

$$(1-x)^{-1/2} = \sum_{n=0}^{\infty} \binom{-\frac{1}{2}}{n}(-x)^n, \quad \text{for } |x| < 1,$$

where

$$\binom{-\frac{1}{2}}{n} = \frac{(-\frac{1}{2})(-\frac{3}{2})(-\frac{5}{2})\cdots(-\frac{1}{2}-n+1)}{n!}.$$

Hence

$$(1-x)^{-1/2}$$

$$= 1 + \tfrac{1}{2}x + \tfrac{3}{8}x^2 + \cdots + (-1)^n \binom{-\frac{1}{2}}{n} x^n + \cdots,$$

for $|x| < 1$.

(b) We know that

$$\frac{d}{dx}\sin^{-1} x = \frac{1}{\sqrt{1-x^2}}.$$

By part (a), with x replaced by x^2, we have

$$\frac{1}{\sqrt{1-x^2}}$$

$$= 1 + \tfrac{1}{2}x^2 + \tfrac{3}{8}x^4 + \cdots + (-1)^n \binom{-\frac{1}{2}}{n} x^{2n} + \cdots,$$

for $|x| < 1$. Hence, by the Integration Rule,

$$\sin^{-1} x = x + \tfrac{1}{6}x^3 + \tfrac{3}{40}x^5 + \cdots$$

$$\quad + \frac{(-1)^n}{2n+1}\binom{-\frac{1}{2}}{n}x^{2n+1} + \cdots,$$

for $|x| < 1$, since $\sin^{-1} 0 = 0$.

Remark By equation (4.2), the coefficients in this Taylor series can be written as

$$\frac{(-1)^n}{2n+1}\binom{-\frac{1}{2}}{n} = \frac{1 \cdot 3 \cdot 5 \cdot \cdots \cdot (2n-1)}{2^n n! (2n+1)}.$$

Index